CUTTING EDGE

UPPER INTERMEDIATE

WORKBOOK

jane comyns carr   frances eales

Longman

Vocabulary

Phrasal verbs to talk about your life map

1 a) This is the beginning of an interview with a South African journalist. Read the text and answer these questions:

Which was the happiest part of his life?

....

Which was the saddest?

....

'I was born just outside Johannesburg, in South Africa. I **grew up** on a farm: I didn't move to Johannesburg until I was nineteen. I remember those years on the farm with great affection. I have two younger sisters and an older brother, and our parents **brought** us **up** to be independent and freethinking. My father always encouraged me to write, and I used to read my stories to him in the evening as he sat outside with a beer. I remember my parents never having much money, but somehow my mother **got by** on the little they had, and made sure we had enough to eat, clothes to wear and books to read.

When I first moved to Johannesburg, to try to get my work published, I was extremely lonely and had no money. As I got more and more depressed, I started drinking a lot, and had several unsuccessful relationships with women. I was very low when I met Rachel, and she helped me to **get through** that difficult period. After I'd been with her for nearly a year, I felt that I really wanted to **settle down** – buy a house, start a family. I even **took up** skateboarding – a great way to get exercise and fresh air!'

b) Look at the six phrasal verbs in **bold** in the text and try to guess their meaning.

c) Put each phrasal verb in the space next to its definition from the *Longman Dictionary of Contemporary English*.

1 *grow up* .... to develop from being a child to being an adult

2 .... to come to the end of a difficult or unpleasant experience or period of time

3 .... to educate and care for a child until it is grown up

4 .... to start living in a place with the intention of staying there, especially after you have travelled a lot

5 .... to have enough money to buy the things you need, but no more

6 .... to become interested in a particular activity or subject and spend time doing it

d) Rewrite the following sentences using the phrasal verbs from the text. Make sure the form of the verb stays the same.

1 I remember *spending my childhood* in a small village near a big lake.

I remember *growing up in a small village near a big lake* .

2 In 1998 I had no job and I got divorced. I don't know how I *survived* the year.

I don't know how I ....

3 My husband's *begun to spend time* jogging because he was so unfit.

My husband's ....

4 It wasn't until he was forty-five that my brother *established a home in one place*.

It wasn't until ....

5 Brian lost his job last month and his wife's having a baby: how will they *buy everything they need*?

How will ....

6 I was *looked after and educated* by my grandparents.

I was ....

e) Complete the sentences below so that they are true for you.

1 I grew up in ....

2 The best age for people to settle down is ....

3 I can get by on .... a month if I have to.

4 The most difficult time I ever had to get through was when

....

5 I was brought up by ....

6 I'd love to take up ....

Reading

2 **a)** Read the following extracts quickly and decide who had the worst experience.

A Date With Disaster?

**Have you ever been on a first date with someone you really liked and found that it turned into a disaster before your very eyes?
We interviewed two people who have had just this experience.**

CELINE, 27
Hairdresser

The worst first date I've ever had was while I was on holiday in Majorca. I must have been about 17, and I met this gorgeous Spanish waiter, Rodrigo. He was a good ten years older than me and had dark brown eyes and black curly hair. Well, after we'd had a few drinks in a local bar, he suggested going for a romantic walk along the beach. Things seemed to be going quite well, even though we didn't have much in common. Then we noticed a group of people standing at the water's edge, staring at something on the beach. We went nearer to see what was happening, and then I got the shock of my life – it was a dead body which had come in with the tide! I turned away immediately, but Rodrigo seemed fascinated by it, and started talking very fast in Spanish to the other people. I found their morbid interest so tasteless that I just walked away … I never dated Rodrigo again, as you can imagine.

ROBERT BUCKLEY, 24
Fitness Instructor

She was someone I knew from school and I'd always really fancied her. I had just got a new motorbike, a Suzuki 250, which I was really proud of. So anyway, one Saturday afternoon, I asked her to come out for a ride, and we went up to a disused airfield a few kilometres away. There was no one else around, so I started driving with one wheel in the air and going really fast. Claire said she loved it and could she have a go at riding it. I couldn't see why not – but how wrong can you be?

Once she'd managed to start it and stay upright, she suddenly got a bit over-confident and zoomed off at top speed towards some trees. As I started running after her, I could see that she was losing control of the bike, and a minute later – bang! She went straight into a tree. Claire was a bit shocked and bruised, but my beautiful Suzuki was a wreck and cost me a fortune to repair. We did see each other again, but from then on we stuck to public transport.

b) Answer these questions by choosing the correct name: Celine, Rodrigo, Robert or Claire.

1 Who had a date by the sea?
   Celine and Rodrigo

2 Who had known the other person for some time before the date?
   ....

3 Who wanted to impress the person they dated?
   ....

4 Who was much older than the person they dated?
   ....

5 Who had an accident?
   ....

6 Who was disgusted by the other person's behaviour?
   ....

7 Whose date was very expensive?
   ....

8 Who went out with the person again?
   ....

c) You can use reading to improve your vocabulary by noticing common phrases (instead of single words) in the text. In the following phrases, underline the correct word without looking back at the text, then look back and check.

1 Robert was really proud *for / of* his new Suzuki 250.

2 Claire asked if she could *have / take* a go at riding the bike.

3 She got over-confident and *lost / hadn't* control of the bike.

4 Celine and Rodrigo went *for / to* a romantic walk along the beach.

5 They didn't *have / think* much in common.

6 When Celine saw the body, she got *a / the* shock of her life.

Grammar check-up

Verb forms

3 **a)** **Match each picture with a sentence.**

a   When I feel really stressed, I usually *take* Einstein for a walk.

b   If I *won* the lottery, I*'d buy* a new house.

c   Jones *was feeling* pleased with himself because he'*d killed* his first bear.

d   At the moment I'*m doing* the washing-up.

e   I'm looking forward to tonight – I *haven't been* to a disco for a long time.

f   I *won't cook* dinner until you *tell* me where the cat is.

g   What a pity! If only I *had* my skates with me!

h   Don't forget the wine. We'*re having* the Simpsons for dinner tonight.

b) **Using the same verb forms, complete these sentences so that they are true for you.**

1   When I feel .... I usually ....
....

2   If I won the lottery, I ....
....

3   This time last year / month / week I was feeling
.... because I'd / hadn't ....
....

4   At the moment I'm ....
....

5   I haven't ....
.... for a long time.

6   I won't .... until ....
.... !

7   If only I .... !

8   I'm .... tonight.

Present Perfect or Past Simple

4 Tick (✓) the best ending for each of the sentences below.

1 I've been to the Pompidou Centre twice
   a   while I was in Paris.
   b   so I don't really want to go there again. ✓

2 Denise and Adam have been married for fifteen years
   a   and they were very happy.
   b   and they're very happy.

3 I lost my car keys –
   a   I can't find them anywhere.
   b   I couldn't find them anywhere.

4 How long have you lived on your own
   a   in this flat?
   b   before you met Lisa?

5 Steve's been very depressed
   a   last week.
   b   all week.

6 John worked for the company for ten years
   a   and we're sorry that he's leaving.
   b   and we were sorry when he left.

Present Perfect or Past Perfect

5 Put the correct form of *have* in the gaps, e.g. *have / haven't, has / hasn't, had / hadn't.*

a   Paul failed his driving test because he *hadn't* practised enough.

b   Henry .... had backache for nearly a year before his wife made him go to the doctor.

c   I'm feeling a bit upset because I .... had some bad news about my brother.

d   Carla says she .... sent the e-mail, but I'm sure she .... because I've checked three times and it's not there.

e   The boys' clothes were filthy – they .... been playing football in the rain.

f   I hope Mrs Reynolds .... remembered to feed the cat – she's very forgetful.

g   I thought I .... left the report on my desk, but I can't find it anywhere.

h   Pierre .... been working with me for several months, but he still can't remember my surname.

Past Simple, Present Perfect or Past Perfect

6 Underline the correct verb form in these two texts.

(A)

Hooliganism

Twenty-five-year-old father of two, Joseph Willis (1) *appeared / has appeared / had appeared* in court yesterday, charged with attacking a police officer. The incident (2) *happened / has happened / had happened* outside the ground after the match between Arsenal and Liverpool. Willis, a passionate Liverpool supporter, (3) *started / has started / had started* a fight with Arsenal fans because his team (4) *lost / has lost / had lost* the match. The judge (5) *gave / has given / had given* him a £200 fine.

(B)

Jackie Lane: Live Tonight!

'My next guest (1) *never had / has never had / had never had* any problems with getting what he wanted. Can you believe that, when he first came to Australia, he (2) *didn't have / hasn't had / hadn't had* a bank account and now he (3) *became / has become / had become* one of the richest people in the world. From 1986–1998 he (4) *managed / has managed / had managed* two international finance companies, and recently he (5) *wrote / has written / had written* a bestselling guide: *10 Steps to Success*. Let's find out how he does it ...'

Pronunciation
Nouns and verbs

LOOK!

Many nouns are the same as verbs:

• *an attack / to attack / respect / to respect*

Usually their pronunciation is the same, but there are some common nouns that change their stress when they become verbs:

• *a decrease – to decrease*

Remember that a dictionary can help you to find where the stress is. This symbol ' means that the stress is on the following syllable:

• /ˈdiːkriːs/ n   /dɪˈkriːs/ v

If a noun and verb are pronounced the same then the pronunciation will be given after the first entry only: e.g. control /kənˈtrəʊl/ n

2 a) Read the words in phonemic script below and mark the stress with a circle above the nouns and verbs in the chart.

/ˈdiːkriːs/ n	/dɪˈkriːs/ v	/ˈrekɔːd/ n	/rɪˈkɔːd/ v
/səˈpɔːt/ n	/səˈpɔːt/ v	/ˈɪnsʌlt/ n	/ɪnˈsʌlt/ v
/kənˈtrəʊl/ n	/kənˈtrəʊl/ v	/ˈdæmɪdʒ/ n	/ˈdæmɪdʒ/ v
/ˈɪnkriːs/ n	/ɪnˈkriːs/ v	/ˈtrænspɔːt/ n	/trænˈspɔːt/ v
/ˈprɒmɪs/ n	/ˈprɒmɪs/ v	/səˈpraɪz/ n	/səˈpraɪz/ v
/ˈɪmpɔːt/ n	/ɪmˈpɔːt/ v	/ˈekspɔːt/ n	/ɪkˈspɔːt/ v

noun	verb	noun	verb
decrease	decrease	record	record
support	support	insult	insult
control	control	damage	damage
increase	increase	transport	transport
promise	promise	surprise	surprise
import	import	export	export

b) 📟 Listen and repeat some of the pairs of nouns and verbs in sentences.

Improve your writing
Spelling

-ible / -able adjectives

LOOK!

We drop the final -e from the verb to make the adjective:

• *move – movable*

When a verb ends with -ce or -ge, we keep the e:

• *replace – replaceable*

3 a) Seven of these spellings are incorrect. Correct them. The first has been done for you.

chang*e*able	valuable	desirable
sociable	manageable	noticible
flexable	miserable	unreasonable
believeable	washible	incredable
adviseable	responsible	adaptable

-ent / -ant adjectives

b) Fill in the missing letter, e or a. Use a dictionary to help you – there is no rule for this!

relev *a* nt	obedi _ nt	confid _ nt
independ _ nt	urg _ nt	effici _ nt
innoc _ nt	unpleas _ nt	arrog _ nt
inconveni _ nt	inconsist _ nt	incompet _ nt

-er / -or

LOOK!

We often add -er or -or to a verb to mean the person who does a job:

• *teach – teacher*

c) Add -r, -er or -or to the verbs below to make jobs.
e.g. *teacher*

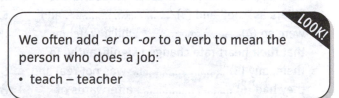

teach	supervise	translate
interpret	train	operate
interview	direct	act
invent	manage	report

Listen and read

What makes you anxious?

4 **a)** Which of the following situations would make you the most anxious?

1 Walking up a dark street alone at night.

2 Giving a speech to a large group of people.

3 Being late for something.

4 Waiting to see the dentist.

5 Waiting for someone who is late.

b) 🔊 Read and / or listen to this extract from *The Way Up to Heaven* by Roald Dahl.

1 Which of the above situations makes Mrs Foster the most anxious? ....

2 Does her husband's behaviour make it better or worse? ....

c) Choose the correct answer (a, b or c).

1 Mrs Foster's fear of missing a train or plane was so strong that
   a it made her ill.
   b it was like an illness. ✓
   c it made her throw things.

2 She got so nervous that a muscle in her eye began to tremble and
   a didn't stop until she'd been travelling for at least an hour.
   b stopped as soon as she was on the train or plane.
   c didn't stop until just before she caught the plane.

3 Mrs Foster used to spend the half hour before it was time to leave
   a walking around, waiting for her husband.
   b waiting for the lift with her husband.
   c walking from room to room with her husband.

4 Mr Foster
   a didn't know how anxious his wife could become.
   b wanted to cause his wife pain.
   c probably kept his wife waiting deliberately.

5 Mrs Foster
   a believed that Mr Foster would never try to hurt her.
   b was beginning to think that Mr Foster might want to hurt her.
   c thought that Mr Foster's unreasonable behaviour was his only weakness.

All her life, Mrs Foster had had such a strong fear of missing a train, a plane, a boat or even the start of a play that her fear was almost an illness. In other respects, she was not a particularly nervous woman, but just the thought of being late on occasions like these
5 used to throw her into a terrible state. As a result, a small muscle in the corner of her left eye would begin to tremble. It was not very much, but the annoying thing was that the problem refused to disappear until an hour or so after the train or plane – or whatever it was – had been safely caught.
10 It is really strange how in certain people a simple fear about a thing like catching a train can grow into serious anxiety. At least half an hour before it was time to leave the house for the station, Mrs Foster used to step out of the lift all ready to go, and then, as she was unable to sit down, she used to move about from room to room
15 until her husband, who must have known about her state of mind, finally joined her and suggested in a cool dry voice that perhaps they had better go now, had they not?

Mr Foster may possibly have had a right to be annoyed by this silliness of his wife's, but he could have had no excuse for increasing
20 her anxiety by keeping her waiting unnecessarily. It is not, of course, certain that this is what he did, but whenever they were going somewhere, his timing was so exact – just a minute or two late, you understand – and his manner so calm that it was hard to believe that he was not purposely causing pain to the unhappy lady.
25 He must have known that she would never dare to call out and tell him to hurry. He had trained her too well for that. He must also have known that if he was prepared to wait just a little longer than was wise, he could make her nearly crazy. On one or two special occasions in the later years of their married life, it seemed almost as
30 though he had wanted to miss the train, simply to increase the poor woman's suffering.

If the husband was guilty, what made his behaviour doubly unreasonable was the fact that, with the exception of this one small weakness, Mrs Foster was, and always had been a good and loving
35 wife. For over thirty years, she had served him loyally and well. There was no doubt about this. Even she knew it, and although she had for years refused to let herself believe that Mr Foster would ever consciously hurt her, there had been times recently when she had begun to wonder.

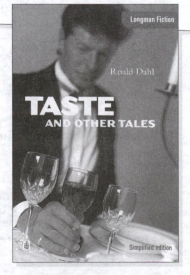

Abstract and general ideas

Gerunds (-*ing* forms)

5 **a)** Complete this article about executive stress using the verbs in the box in a *positive* or *negative* gerund form.

> drink (x 2)   get   eat (x 2)   go (x 2)   talk   take (x 2)

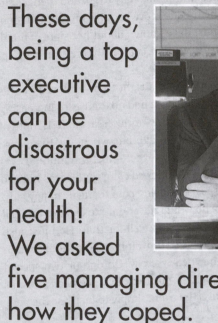

These days, being a top executive can be disastrous for your health! We asked five managing directors how they coped.

Their top ten tips for ways of keeping healthy and stress-free are:

- ☐ ....*going*........ to the gym three times a week.
- ☐ .... sensibly.
- ☐ .... alcohol at lunch.
- ☐ .... work home.
- ☐ .... at least 7 hours' sleep each night.
- ☐ .... about business at home.
- ☐ .... mineral water instead of strong coffee.
- ☐ .... a daily 'power nap'.
- ☐ .... to bed after 11 o'clock during the week.
- ☐ .... fattening snacks between meals.

b) Complete the second sentence so that it has a similar meaning to the first one, using a gerund.

a   It can be expensive to eat out.
Eating out can be .... expensive.

b   I find it easy to make new friends.
.... easy.

c   I hate it when I don't remember people's names.
I hate ....

d   Jack worked for twelve hours in the office and then he decided to go home.
.... Jack decided to go home.

e   My mother-in-law can't stand people who smoke when she's eating.
My mother-in-law ....

f   I find that a good way to relax is to have a nice long bath.
.... a good way to relax.

Grammar snack

Be / get used to + noun or gerund

Felipe comes from Brazil.	Felipe arrives in England to study …	One month later …	Two months later …

LOOK!

He**'s used to** hot weather.
(It's normal for him)

He**'s not used to** the rain.
(It's new and strange for him)

He**'s getting used to** the rain.
(It's becoming more normal for him)

He**'s got used to** the rain.
(It's no longer strange for him)

However, his friend Pablo **can't get used to** the rain.

(He has tried to feel more comfortable with it, but it's still a problem for him)

Here are some more examples:

• *I'm not used to this computer programme.*
• *You'll soon get used to driving on the left.*

• *I'm used to going to bed early.*
• *I can't get used to cooking for myself.*

6 a) Simon has recently started working in Cairo. Look at these extracts from two of his letters and decide if the statements are *T* (true) or *F* (false).

Ⓐ

September 1, Cairo

… and I'm living in a flat on a very noisy street, which is no problem after living in the centre of Manchester. The only thing is, I'm finding it a bit difficult to share with two other people, having lived on my own for so long. I seem to be irritable all the time, and the heat doesn't help – it's so much hotter than I expected, almost unbearable, in fact. The people here are really friendly, but they do stare at me a lot, maybe because of my red hair, which I find odd …

Ⓑ

November 8, Cairo

… I'm enjoying life here much more now. The heat's not nearly such a problem, as long as I avoid the midday sun. I love going to buy food at the wonderful covered market, although they expect me to argue about the prices, and I still find that strange! The only real problem is that my flat's opposite a mosque, and I wake up at 2 a.m. every morning because of the call to prayer – I don't think I'll ever be able to sleep through the night.

Ⓐ

1 Simon is used to living in a noisy place. ....*T*....

2 Simon is used to flat-sharing. ....

3 Simon isn't used to the heat. ....

4 Simon is used to people staring at him. ....

Ⓑ

5 Simon is getting used to the heat. ....

6 Simon is used to arguing about food prices. ....

7 Simon thinks he'll get used to waking up at 2 a.m. every morning. ....

15

b) Rewrite the two sentences to make a single sentence using *be / get used to* + gerund or noun.

1 Jeff's working at night this month. It's a big problem for him.

Jeff's *not used to working at night* .

2 I found Sally's Irish accent strange at first. Now I can understand it better.

I ....

3 Everyone eats very late at night. Linda finds this strange.

Linda ....

4 People bow when they meet. I've been here for ten years and I still find it odd.

I can't ....

5 I find the weather here really strange. I always will.

I'll never ....

c) Answer these questions, using *be / get used to*.

1

Why should the British be careful the first time they drive abroad?

Because they *'re not used to driving on the right*.

2

Why do the Chinese find it strange to eat with a knife and fork?

Because they …

3

Are contact lenses uncomfortable?

Yes, until …

4

Why do the British often get burnt when they sunbathe on the beach?

Because they …

5

Is a big motorbike dangerous?

It can be, until …

Prefixes

7 a) Find eleven more words with prefixes in the word box. Use the clues to help you.

I	M	P	A	T	I	E	N	T	S	R	K
L	U	X	T	C	T	U	N	E	V	E	N
L	O	W	F	A	T	C	E	Q	P	P	Z
E	C	E	E	A	M	I	S	R	E	A	D
G	K	L	O	M	B	E	V	E	P	Y	S
I	S	L	I	I	X	N	A	P	U	T	E
B	A	K	R	S	I	O	W	L	S	A	Y
L	O	N	Y	S	W	N	I	A	N	U	N
E	C	O	U	P	A	S	A	Y	E	N	O
K	O	W	T	E	N	T	I	D	A	F	A
N	O	N	A	L	C	O	H	O	L	I	C
O	D	D	B	L	O	P	A	I	N	T	S

1 Don't cycle too fast, the road's very u n e v e n along here.

2 My doctor's handwriting is so bad, it's _ _ _ _ _ _ _ _ _ .

3 We got very _ _ _ _ _ _ _ _ _ waiting for the bus.

4 Haven't you heard of Minnie Driver? She's very _ _ _ _ - _ _ _ _ _ .

5 I'm on a _ _ _ - _ _ _ diet, so I can't eat butter or cheese.

6 Have you got anything _ _ _ - _ _ _ _ _ _ _ _ _ to drink? I'm driving.

7 I'm sorry, I always _ _ _ _ _ _ _ _ your name – is it with a y?

8 We've been working _ _ _ - _ _ _ _ since eight this morning. Let's have a break.

9 Martin _ _ _ _ _ _ _ the instructions and washed the shirt in hot water instead of warm.

10 Could you _ _ _ _ _ _ that part of the video? I didn't see the goal.

11 How are you going to _ _ _ _ _ the loan, Sir? In monthly instalments?

12 I'm feeling really _ _ _ _ _ at the moment, I haven't been to the gym for weeks.

b) Notice that the prefix is not usually stressed:

●   ●
impatient   illegible

⊟ Listen to the sentences and repeat them.

Responding sympathetically in writing

8 **a)** Which of these three situations is the letter below responding to? ....

A

A friend writes to tell you that she's split up with her fiancé and that she's worried because she's in the same class as him at college. Also, she can't concentrate on studying for her exams.

B

A friend writes to tell you that she's lost her job and she's worried that she's too old to find a new job easily, and the effect that it will have on her family.

C

A friend writes to tell you that she's failed her final exam at university and therefore will not get the job she had been offered. She's worried about telling her family and about paying back the money she borrowed in order to study.

---

25 Cedar Avenue,
Macclesfield,
Cheshire
15th September, 200-

Dear Brigitte,

Thanks for your letter. (1) ...I was so sorry to hear your news............... ,it was quite a shock because I know how hard you've been studying recently. (2) .... , especially because of how your family might react — but do you really need to tell them yet?

(3) .... about the job — after all, from what you say, they haven't made a definite decision yet. (4) .... finances, but I'm sure the bank will understand if you explain the situation.

(5) .... You'd be welcome to come and stay at my house for a while

(6) .... with your finances. Do keep in touch — give me a ring if you want to talk it over.

love,
Sylvie

---

b) Complete the gaps in the letter with the correct phrases from the box.

- Is there anything at all I can do?
- I was so sorry to hear your news
- if that would help
- It sounds like a really difficult situation
- Try not to worry too much
- I know you must be really worried about

c) Write a letter responding to one of the other two situations above. Try to use some of the expressions in the box.

module 3

Vocabulary

Verb and adverb combinations

1 Philip is staying in Lisbon with his friend, Juao. Read this extract from his letter and write the correct adverb (a, b or c) in the gap.

Last Saturday night was quite eventful. Juao and I were wandering (1) around........... in the old part of the town, when he suggested going to a new restaurant that had just opened in the area.

He wasn't quite sure where it was, so we went (2) .... a group of teenagers standing on a street corner, to ask for directions. Well, I don't know what they had to hide, but as soon as they saw us, they just ran (3) ....! "They must have thought you were a policeman," Juao joked. Anyway, we found the restaurant by chance, as we were walking (4) .... a little side street. It looked very cosy and had an interesting menu, so we got ourselves a table and chose our food. We were just ordering some wine, when the waiter suddenly looked towards the kitchen, then walked (5) ...., without a word of explanation. A few minutes later, he came (6) .... our table and explained, in a very quiet voice, that there was a slight problem in the kitchen, and that our meal might be delayed. Just as he said that, the other waiters started rushing (7) ...., looking panicky. The people sitting near the kitchen suddenly got up and started running (8) ...., shouting as they passed our table, "The kitchen's on fire!" We thought we'd better follow them and quickly left the restaurant. Outside, we decided to go to Juao's house and cook something there. We waited for ages for a taxi, and when one finally stopped, he said that Juao's house was too far out of his way, and drove (9) ....! So in the end we walked (10) .... and bought a hamburger on the way.

1 a away	b around	c up
2 a along	b off	c up to
3 a along	b off	c out
4 a along	b on	c away
5 a off	b up	c in
6 a around	b up to	c up
7 a up to	b along	c around
8 a away	b towards	c along
9 a around	b off	c up
10 a to home	b at home	c home

Reading

A short break in Copenhagen

2 a) Before you read the extract on the opposite page from a travel brochure, write down two things you know about Copenhagen.

1 ....

....

2 ....

....

b) Read the text and answer the following questions to a travel agent.

1 Is it necessary to hire a car while we're there?

....

2 My son says that you can visit the place where Carlsberg beer is made. Is that true?

....

3 Where's the best place to go shopping?

....

4 I don't want to stay in a big hotel, I find them too impersonal. Which one do you suggest?

....

5 I'd like to stay in a hotel near the harbour. Where do you recommend?

....

6 I'd like to visit the castle where *Hamlet* is set. Is that possible on a Saturday in March?

....

7 How much would it cost to stay in the cheapest hotel for two nights in October?

....

8 How much is a taxi from the airport to the city centre and how long does it take?

....

Copenhagen

Although capital of one of Europe's smallest countries, the clean and friendly city of Copenhagen offers a host of cultural and sightseeing opportunities. With a vast number of pedestrianised streets, the best way to sightsee is by foot, or you may prefer a leisurely canal cruise past the colourful waterfront houses.

Sights not to be missed include Rosenborg Castle which houses the Crown Jewels, Amalienborg Palace, the Little Mermaid and, of course, the famous Tivoli Gardens with a myriad of restaurants and bars, concert halls and a fairground offering something for everyone. Also worth a visit is the Viking Museum and for something different why not tour the Carlsberg Brewery.

Shoppers will enjoy the fine shops of the Stroget and don't forget the side-streets leading from it. After sunset head for Nyhavn quayside.

My comment:

"A rarity among capital cities – it does not overwhelm you, but rather takes you gently in and shows you its sights with quiet pride. The Little Mermaid is smaller than you imagined (but she is, after all, 'Little') and there isn't a single inch of neon among the light bulbs of Tivoli."

John Carter

1 HOTEL MAYFAIR

This comfortable hotel is located in the heart of the city, just a few minutes from Tivoli Gardens.

Breakfast room ♦ bar ♦ 102 English-style rooms with en suite facilities, colour television, hairdryer, mini bar and telephone

2 HOTEL SAVOY

Copenhagen's many attractions are all within easy reach of this small, friendly hotel.

Breakfast room ♦ courtyard cafe ♦ bar ♦ 66 rooms with private facilities, colour television, mini bar, radio and telephone

3 HOTEL ADMIRAL

A characteristic hotel within a half-timbered building, ideally situated in the centre of Copenhagen close to the Royal Palace, Theatre and the harbour.

Restaurant ♦ bar ♦ nightclub ♦ 363 rooms with en suite facilities, colour television, hairdryer and telephone

PRICES are in £'s per person, sharing a twin / double room, departing from GATWICK with BRITISH AIRWAYS.									
Hotel Name	Savoy			Mayfair			Admiral		
Holiday No	10802			10800			10804		
No of Nights in hotel	1	2	Extra Night	1	2	Extra Night	1	2	Extra Night
01 Jan - 31 Mar	205	238	31	216	258	42	212	252	38
01 Jan - 13 Apr	238	269	31	249	291	42	245	285	38
14 Apr - 29 Apr	238	269	31	249	291	42	266	326	60
30 Apr - 30 Sep	252	298	45	252	298	45	266	326	60
01 Oct - 31 Oct	239	273	32	251	295	44	266	326	60
01 Nov - 31 Dec	239	273	32	251	295	44	247	289	40
Single Supp (per night)	26			30			41		

HOTEL INFORMATION - Mon-Thur supplements (in £'s per adult, per night):-
Admiral - 01 Jan - 02 Apr & 01 Nov - 11 Dec - £21 in a twin/double or £38 in a single
Mayfair - 01 May - 30 Sep - £7 in a twin/double or £13 in a single
Superior room supplements (in £'s per adult, per night) - Mayfair - £14 in a twin/double or a single;
(except Mon-Thur between 30 Apr - 30 Sep - £20 in a twin/double; £26 in a single.)

ALTERNATIVE HOTELS
Premier Holidays are able to offer additional hotels in Copenhagen - please ask for details.

ONE OR TWO NIGHT STAYS - must include a Saturday night

TRANSFER OPTIONS - Transfers between the airport and your hotel are not included.
As a guide we have listed examples of the public transport available:-
AIRPORT/CITY - Airport Shuttle bus to city centre - £5.00; journey - 20 mins;
                   Taxi - £18.00; journey - 15 mins

CITY & HARBOUR TOUR – £18
This 2½ hour tour begins with a coach tour passing Tivoli Gardens, New Carlsberg Glypolel and the Gefion Fountain, then by boat past the Little Mermaid and along the picturesque canals to Christianshavn
DEPARTS - Daily between 13 Jun - 13 Sep

CASTLE TOUR OF NORTH SEALAND – £37
A full day tour which includes a visit to Kronborg Castle - the setting for Shakespeare's Hamlet and Fredensborg Castle which is the Queen's summer residence
DEPARTS - Weds & Sun - 01 Jan - 29 Apr & 17 Oct - 31 Dec; Wed, Sat & Sun 02 May - 16 Oct

Grammar check-up

Past Simple, Past Continuous and Past Perfect in narratives

3 Use the prompts to write complete sentences. Choose the best past form of the verb.

1 This / happen / one summer when three of us / travel / around Europe.
This happened one summer ...

....

2 We / walk / around a town when a man / offer / to change our money.

....

3 A friend / warn / us never to change money on the street, but the man / look / honest, so we / decide / to take a chance.

....
....

4 He / pretend / to give me fifty notes but I / notice / that he / only give / me forty-eight, so I / ask / him to count them again.

....
....

5 Ten minutes later we / sit / in a cafe when I / realise / that he / trick / us.

....
....

6 When he / give / me back the money, he / replace / everything except the top two notes with newspaper!

....
.... !

The Present Participle

4 Combine the sentences to make one sentence, using a Present Participle.

a There were crowds of people. They were waiting outside the TV studio.
There were crowds of people waiting outside the TV studio .

b Who's that woman? She's sitting over there.
....
.... ?

c Our next door neighbour saw the burglar. He was climbing through an upstairs window.
....
....
....

d Isn't that your son? He's throwing stones at that car.
....
.... ?

e Pacific Airlines received hundreds of letters. They were enquiring about the free flights offer.
....
....

f From my bedroom I can hear lots of trains. They go by in the middle of the night.
....
....

g I rushed into the kitchen because I could smell the toast. It was burning.
....
....
....

Verb forms in narrative

Past Simple / Continuous, Past Perfect Simple / Continuous, Present Participle

5 These letters about life's biggest disappointments were sent to a teenage magazine. Complete each gap with a verb from the boxes in the correct form.

Liz, aged twelve

My sister (1) ...cancelled......... her wedding three days before it was due to happen. I (2) .... to make her change her mind because I (3) .... to wearing the dress that my mum (4) .... for me. On the day she was supposed to get married I (5) .... into her room while she (6) .... a bath and (7) .... her favourite dress into little pieces.

| try go cut make cancel look forward have |

Joseph, aged eleven

We (8) .... the lottery for years and we (9) .... anything, so when my dad (10) .... a fake lottery ticket with the winning numbers from the night before on it, we (11) .... believe our luck! Later, when we (12) .... what to spend the money on, he (13) .... us the truth and my mum (14) .... to him for weeks!

| make not win tell not speak do can plan |

Continuous aspect in other tenses

6 In six of the sentences below the tenses are wrong. Find the mistakes and correct them. One has been done for you.

a I'm agreeing with you about the delivery dates.
   I agree

b The Publicity Department are having a few problems at the moment – all the computers are down.

c Don't ring my home number over the weekend because I'll stay at Donald's house.

d Hello, how are you? Oh! You've been changing your hairstyle.

e This wine is tasting a bit strange – where's it from?

f We'll be giving away free samples of shampoo all next week.

g I'm sorry I haven't written for so long, but …

h My car's just round the corner, I'll be giving you a lift.

i I must sit down for a minute – I've been rushing around all day.

j Matt paints his room, that's why all the furniture's on the balcony.

Pronunciation

Contractions and weak forms

7 a) 🔊 Listen to six answerphone messages and write them in the spaces below. Remember, contractions count as two words, e.g. *I'll = I will*.

1 Daniel here – *I'll be working late tonight so don't wait up for me* .
(13 words)

2 This is Helen – ....
....
....
.... (17 words)

3 It's Peter Crawford – ....
....
....
.... (19 words)

4 This is Jenny McAdam – ....
....
....
.... (20 words)

5 Anna, it's Roger – ....
....
....
.... (15 words)

6 This is Simpson's Fabric
   Department – ....
....
....
.... (12 words)

b) 🔊 Try to say the sentences at the same time as the cassette, paying attention to stress and contracted and weak forms.

Grammar snack

so / such

8 a) Here are some complaints about holidays. Decide if they are about a hotel (H), a train station (S), or a day-trip (DT).

1 I've never had **such awful food**, or known **such rude waiters**. .....H....

2 The announcements were **so unclear** – we had no idea which platform to go to. ....

3 We had **so little time** to look around that it wasn't worth getting off the bus. It was **such a waste of money**. ....

4 It was **such a long way** from the sea, we had to get a bus. ....

5 He was driving **so quickly**, it was impossible to take a photo. ....

6 There were **so many people** that I couldn't get on the train. ....

> **LOOK!**
>
> Look at the grammar with *so / such* in **bold** in the sentences above.
>
> | **so** | unclear | (adjective) |
> | | quickly | (adverb) |
> | | many / few people | (quantifier + countable noun) |
> | | much / little time | (quantifier + uncountable noun) |
> | **such** | a waste of money | (noun) |
> | | a long way | (adjective + countable noun) |
> | | rude waiters | (adjective + plural noun) |
> | | awful food | (adjective + uncountable noun) |

b) Put *so*, *such* and *such a* in front of these words and phrases.

......*so*........ expensive   .... mess

.... slowly   .... loud music

.... much traffic   .... comfortable beds

.... friendly tour guide .... few places to eat

c) Complete these sentences with a word or phrase from the box below, and add *so*, *such*, *such a*, *so many* or *so much*.

> terrible weather   bad   good time   times   crowded   information

1 The traffic was *so bad*........................ that we missed our flight.

2 We don't usually have .... at this time of year.

3 Everyone had .... at the barbecue.

4 They didn't expect the exhibition to be ....

5 Janet's seen the film .... that she knows every line.

6 There was .... in the report that I didn't have time to read it.

Improve your writing

Avoiding repetition

9 **a)** Read this extract from a travel guide to Tokyo and:

- underline any repetition of words or phrases
- cross out any words or phrases which can be omitted

TOKYO / 317

Tokyo

In the past few years, Tokyo has had more than Tokyo's fair share of problems – the financial problems in particular have left Tokyo far less confident than Tokyo was in the mid-1980s.

The good news, though, is that Tokyo is great value for money. Recently, visitors have found that Tokyo has cheaper train fares and has cheaper shops than comparable cities in Europe have. The best way to start a tour is with an early visit to the fish and vegetable market, which is called Tsukiji. A visit to the market is a good way to wake up, with all the market's noises and smells. Then satisfy your hunger with a plate of fish at one of the many lively fish restaurants around the market. If Japanese people want a peaceful escape from the crowds, Japanese people go to nearby Hama Rikyu Teien, a peaceful traditional garden which is designed around small lakes. Then, if you want a complete contrast, try the glamorous shopping district, Ginza, but if you don't want a complete contrast, there are always more gardens at Shinjuku Gyoen.

b) Some of the words repeated in the text can be replaced with these alternatives in the box. Decide where to put them.

| the capital   difficulties   the city   less expensive   seafood   tranquil |

the capital
e.g. … in particular have left Tokyo far less confident …

c) Rewrite the text to make it sound more natural. Remember that you can do this by using pronouns and omitting words.

module 4

Vocabulary

Qualities of mind

1 a) Complete the chart with the missing nouns and adjectives. Use a dictionary if necessary. Note that each group has an ending in common.

noun	adjective
creativity	creative
....	popular
....	dependable
....	imaginative
....	determined
....	lonely
....	impulsive
....	inventive
....	stubborn
....	awkward
art	....
science	....
intelligence	....
confidence	....
brilliance	....
emotion	....
logic	....

b) Complete these sentences from a discussion about candidates for a job. Use nouns and adjectives from the chart.

1 Monica would be very *popular*........... with her colleagues; we all liked her, didn't we?

2 Tariq showed a lot of .... to get to such a high position at his age. He obviously wants to be really successful.

3 Monica has a really .... mind. I expect she's very good at mathematics.

4 Tariq could be quite .... once he'd made a decision about something. I expect nothing would change his mind.

5 I think Kate's .... is a weak point. She doesn't think before she speaks.

6 Monica had enough .... to disagree with us in the interview. She seemed very sure of herself.

7 Kate was rather .... in the group discussions. She didn't seem to know when or how to join in.

c) Complete these sentences so that they are true for you, using nouns and adjectives from the chart.

1 I hate the idea of being *lonely*............... in my old age.

2 I have a very .... mind.

3 .... is a quality I'd like to have.

4 I think I'm much too ....

5 If only I were more ....

Pronunciation

Stress patterns with suffixes

2 a) 🔲 Listen to these words (or say them aloud) and mark the stressed syllable with a circle.

●

1 creativity

2 popularity

3 dependability

4 imagination

5 determination

6 scientific

7 artistic

8 creative

9 impulsive

10 inventive

b) Underline the correct answer, 1, 2, or 3. When a word ends with *-ity*, *-tion*, *-ic* or *-ive*, we stress:

1 the suffix.

2 the syllable before the suffix.

3 the third syllable.

c) 🔲 Listen to the words and repeat them, paying attention to the stress.

Grammar check-up

Passives quiz

3 a) **Look at the clues in the quiz and find the answer.**

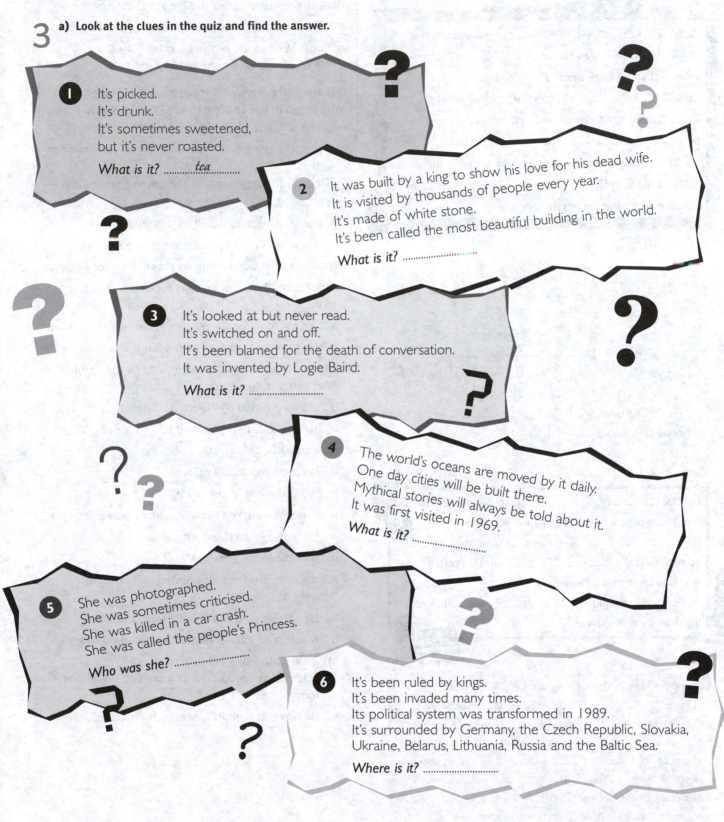

1 It's picked.
It's drunk.
It's sometimes sweetened,
but it's never roasted.

What is it? ....*tea*..........

2 It was built by a king to show his love for his dead wife.
It is visited by thousands of people every year.
It's made of white stone.
It's been called the most beautiful building in the world.

What is it? ....

3 It's looked at but never read.
It's switched on and off.
It's been blamed for the death of conversation.
It was invented by Logie Baird.

What is it? ....

4 The world's oceans are moved by it daily.
One day cities will be built there.
Mythical stories will always be told about it.
It was first visited in 1969.

What is it? ....

5 She was photographed.
She was sometimes criticised.
She was killed in a car crash.
She was called the people's Princess.

Who was she? ....

6 It's been ruled by kings.
It's been invaded many times.
Its political system was transformed in 1989.
It's surrounded by Germany, the Czech Republic, Slovakia, Ukraine, Belarus, Lithuania, Russia and the Baltic Sea.

Where is it? ....

b) **Now write questions for your classmates using the passive.**

Passives

4 Complete the gaps in the texts below with the correct form of the verb in the active or passive.

A

Adfen Plus (1) *is recommended* (recommend) for those times when you (2) .... (need) powerful relief from pain. The tablets (3) .... (specially / formulate) to make them easy to swallow. Each tablet (4) .... (contain) Ibuprofen, BP 200 mg, and aspirin. As with other pain relievers, Adfen Plus should (5) .... (not / take) if you have any stomach disorders.

B

This little known castle (1) .... (only recently / open) its doors to the public, and Qualtours (2) .... (offer) special reductions for this month only. The tour (3) .... (include) the living quarters, the library, the kitchens and the gardens. The size of each tour (4) .... (limit) to twelve people. Bookings may (5) .... (make) in advance by telephone.

C

Licorice (1) .... (use) by mankind for thousands of years. In China in 3000 BC, licorice (2) .... (believe) to have amazing powers and (3) .... (use) in certain religious ceremonies. People (4) .... (believe) that it could (5) .... (protect) the dead from evil spirits.

D

An outbreak of food poisoning at a top London hotel (1) .... (investigate) last night. More than fifteen guests at a business lunch at the Stanmore Hotel (2) .... (complain) of nausea during the afternoon, after they (3) .... (eat) shellfish which doctors later found (4) .... (not / properly / clean). Ten people (5) .... (currently / treat) in hospital, but most of them expect (6) .... (send) home later today.

Choosing active or passive

LOOK!

Look at this sentence:
Walt Disney pioneered full-length cartoons.
Which sentence follows best, **a** or **b**?
a *Snow White was made by him in 1937.*
b *He made Snow White in 1937.* ✓

b is the right answer because we are more interested in the **topic** of Walt Disney, so we make him the **subject** of the second sentence.

5 Tick (✓) the best way of continuing after each sentence.

1 A man has been arrested for hooliganism.
  a He is being held in Dundee police station. ✓
  b They are holding him in Dundee police station.

2 Kirk Blane, the controversial rock star, died last night.
  a An overdose of sleeping pills was taken by him.
  b He took an overdose of sleeping pills.

3 *Night of Passion* has won first prize at the Cannes Film Festival this year.
  a It was directed by Henrietta Calvin.
  b Henrietta Calvin directed it.

4 How much is breakfast?
  a It's included in the price.
  b We include it in the price.

5 A man was attacked outside a local pub last night.
  a He was shot in the chest.
  b Someone shot him in the chest.

6 Alan Curtis has been appointed as Managing Director of Comco.
  a He will be paid a salary of over $500,000.
  b A salary of over $500,000 will be paid to him.

7 My brother-in-law's very rich.
  a A house in Barbados has just been bought by him.
  b He has just bought a house in Barbados.

Improve your writing

Describing a traditional dish

6 **a)** Match the verb to the picture.

chop

grate beat stir drain chop sieve season

b) Here are the lines of an e-mail that Marco sent his teacher, Frances. Write the text in the correct order.

New Message – 1

Send Address Attach Reply Reply All Forward Store Print Delete

☒ Log ☐ Receipt

Normal ▼

Dear Frances,

(A) As soon as it comes to the boil, put the spaghetti in, but **don't** turn the heat down, **or the pasta won't** cook properly (I've often seen English people doing this).

(B) **The next thing to do is** boil lots of salted water in a pan.

(C) Serve it with a good red wine and enjoy!

(D) **You start by preparing** the sauce: cut the bacon into little pieces and brown them on a low heat.

(E) That's it for now. I hope to come back to school after my summer holidays – give my best wishes to any of my classmates who are still there.

(F) **First of all, you'll** need 2 eggs, 20g of smoked bacon (it must be smoked), 20–30g of Parmesan cheese and 100g of spaghetti.

(G) **Next,** grate the cheese as finely as possible and stir it into the egg yolks.

(H) **Then** separate the egg whites from the yolks and beat the yolks in a bowl – **you can add** some salt and pepper at this point, **if you want to.**

(I) However, **make sure you don't** cook it for more than 8 minutes, or it'll be ruined.

(J) Here's that recipe I promised you for spaghetti alla carbonara, the way we *really* make it in Italy – that means *no cream*!

(K) **Now you just** need to drain it and add the bacon and the egg mixture to it. **When you've done this,** you don't need to put it back on the heat, because the egg will cook itself.

Ciao, Marco

c) Write a recipe of a traditional or a favourite dish from your country to send to an English speaking friend. Try to use some of the phrases in **bold** in Marco's recipe.

Listen and read

How to do magic tricks

Here are pictures of four magic tricks that you can do to amaze your friends.

7 a) 📼 Read and / or listen to the texts which describe the magic tricks and then match each picture to the correct text.

Ⓐ

Ask for a volunteer from the group. Say you can tell him his age and how much loose change he has in his pocket, provided it is less than £1 (£1 = 100p). Get him in secret to write down the following:

- his age
- double it
- add 5
- multiply by 50
- subtract 365
- add the amount of change in his pocket (eg 55P)

Ask him for the last number, and in your head add 115. In the final number, the first two figures are always the person's age, and the second two, the amount of change. The formula always works, as long as the change is less than £1.

Ⓑ

Before you do this trick, arrange a pack of cards so that the six of hearts is on the bottom and the five of diamonds is on the top. Ask for a volunteer, and give her the five of hearts and the six of diamonds. Quickly get her to put the cards back into the pack in two different places. Tell her you're going to find the two cards. Shake the pack, blow on it, and say a few 'magic' words, then throw the pack on the table, keeping the bottom and top cards in your hand. Your friends will automatically assume that these are the same cards that were put back into the pack. To make sure that this trick works, don't let your volunteer look too closely at the two original cards, or she'll remember them too well and see through your trick!

Ⓒ

Ask the group to name some famous people. Appear to write the names on slips of paper, whilst in fact only writing the first name you are given, on each piece. Put them all in a hat and ask someone to pick one of them, and fold it, so that you cannot see what is on it. Put all the other slips in an ashtray and set fire to them, muttering 'magic' words and staring at the ashes. Then announce the name on the unburnt slip.

Ⓓ

To do this trick, you can use either freshly-squeezed lemon or onion juice (onion juice should be left to stand for a few minutes, first). Dip a wooden toothpick into the juice, and write a message on a sheet of paper. Show your friends the 'blank' piece of paper, then make the message appear miraculously, by asking a volunteer to hold the paper near a warm light bulb or lighter – be careful not to let it catch fire! Milk can also be used – after it has dried, rub cigarette ash lightly over the paper.

b) When these tricks were performed, people said the following things. Match the people's comments to each trick.

Trick A   ....*6*.....   ....

Trick B   ....

Trick C   ....

Trick D   ....

1   Choose one of the pieces, but don't let me see it.

2   Wait a minute – I didn't get a good look at the cards!

3   Don't hold that flame too close!

4   Can I put them anywhere in the pack?

5   Can you see anything on this paper?

6   How much did you say to take away? 360?

7   … and … it's … Robert Redford!

8   What's 81 times 50?

c) Decide if these pairs of words from the text and the people's comments above have a similar (S) or different (D) meaning. Try to do this without a dictionary, by reading the text carefully. Words from the text are in **bold**.

1   **to subtract** / to take away   ....*S*......

2   **multiplied by** / times   ....

3   **figure** / number   ....

4   **to mutter** / to announce   ....

5   **a slip** / a piece   ....

6   **to set fire to** / to catch fire   ....

Grammar snack

To have / get something done

8 **a)** In these conversations, are the expressions in bold about the past, present or future?

1   Would you like to meet for lunch on Friday?
Sorry, I can't, **I'm having my hair cut** then – what about Thursday?   ......*future*.......

2   I'm so sorry I'm late, **I went to have my eyes checked** and I had to wait for ages.
That's okay, we haven't started yet.   ....

3   Oh no! I'm so sorry – all over your dress!
I'll get it cleaned for you, of course.
No really, it's only an old dress.   ....

4   I'm sorry about the noise, **we're having a new floor put in**. I hope they'll be finished in about an hour.
That's okay, we're just going out.   ....

LOOK!

You use *have / get* + object + Past Participle to say that someone does a service for you, and you probably pay them.

- *I'm having my hair cut*.
- I went to **have** my eyes **checked**.
- *I'll get it cleaned*.
- *We're having a new floor put in*.

Notice: *get* is more informal.

b) Rewrite the following sentences, using the correct form of *have / get* + object + Past Participle.

1   The windows need to be cleaned.
I need to *have / get the windows cleaned*.................... .

2   The shop delivers our newspaper every day.
We ....

3   She made me two photocopies of the article.
I ....

4   A carpenter is putting some shelves up for Susan at the moment.
Susan ....

5   Can you develop this film as quickly as possible?
I need to ....

6   They're printing some business cards for me tomorrow.
I ....

c) Put these questions in the correct order and write answers which are true for you. The first word is underlined.

1   your–often–do–have–How–tested–you–eyes?
How often do you have your eyes tested....................
.... ?

2   ever–fortune–your–told–had–you–Have?
....
.... ?

3   last–When–your–checked–did–have–teeth–you?
....
.... ?

4   have–you–Would–changed–ever–of–your–part–body?
....
.... ?

module 5

Jazz chant

Verb noun word combinations

Repeating word combinations can help you to remember them.

1 📼 Put the words from the boxes into the correct place, then try saying the chant alone or at the same time as the cassette. Notice that lines two and four of each verse always rhyme.

How do you cope with *problems* ....?
How do you cope with ....?
How do you cope with a difficult ....?
Relax, and worry less!

stress   job   problems

First she took over Stephen's ....
Next she took over his ....
Then she took over his ....
There's nothing left to rob!

company   flat   job

Have you achieved something ....?
Have you achieved ....?
Have you achieved your .... in life?
Or is your life a mess?

worthwhile   goals   success

He hated his job as a ....
For years he'd been just a ....
He was too shy to talk to ....
And was really afraid of the dark.

clerk   women   banker

He overcame his .... at work
And he began to make his mark.
He overcame his .... with girls
But not his .... of the dark.

fear   problems   shyness

Dictionary work

Verb noun combinations

LOOK!

Dictionaries can help you to find word combinations:

> **to do something**
> **do** /duː/ [v T] *"What are you doing?" "I'm trying to fix the television."*
> **do work / housework / homework** *95% of housework is done by women.* | *I did a lot of work in the garden today.*
> **do the washing / cooking / shopping etc** *His mother still does all his washing.*
> **do a test / exam / course etc** *He's doing an art course at Wrexham College.*

The *Longman Essential Activator* shows word combinations in **bold**.

2 **a)** Look at these extracts from the same dictionary and find nouns to complete the diagrams on the next page.

to show
show /ʃəʊ/ [v T] to behave in a way that shows people how you feel or what your character is like
show interest / surprise / enthusiasm / anger etc (= show that you are interested, surprised etc) *Paul didn't show much interest in the idea.*
show courage / determination / skill / confidence etc (= show that you are brave, determined etc) *The hostages showed great courage in a very frightening situation.*

to win
win /wɪn/ [v I / T] to win a race, competition, election etc, for example by getting more points, votes etc than everyone else or by being the first to finish: *They don't have much chance of winning.*
win a race / game / election etc *Chang won the first set but lost the next two.* | *The competition was won by a Nigerian.*
win a prize / medal etc *His book won the Pulitzer Prize for literature.* | *She won almost $1 million in the lottery.*

to raise
raise /reɪz/ [v T] to increase prices, taxes etc, or to make certain feelings stronger: *Before the election the President promised not to raise taxes.* | *Oil companies are planning to raise prices.*
raise hopes / expectations (= make people more hopeful)
raise doubts / fears / questions (= make people more uncertain or worried)

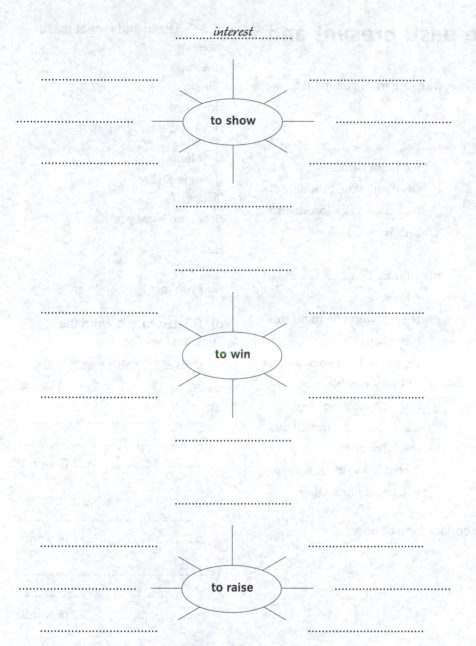

interest

to show

to win

to raise

b) Change these sentences so that they are true about you, or your country, using the verb noun combinations in **bold**.

1   Our government hasn't **raised taxes** this year.
Our government has raised taxes a lot in the last six months .

2   I've never **won a competition**.

....

3   My parents never **showed** any **interest** in my progress at school.

....

4   The Social Democrats **won** the last **election** by a huge majority.

....

5   I never **show anger**, even if I feel something very strongly.

....

6   People have **raised** a lot of **questions** on television about drug problems recently.

....

Future Perfect or Future Simple

3 Underline the correct form in the sentences below.

a   Maria's doing a two-week lecture tour in Russia – when she gets back *she'll visit /* *she'll have visited* ten cities and I'm sure *she'll feel / she'll have felt* absolutely exhausted!

b   My New Year's resolutions are to go on a diet and to stop smoking. This time next year *I'll lose / I'll have lost* weight and *I'll have / I'll have had* more money to spend.

c   Here's the film – *will the photos be / will the photos have been* ready by Thursday?
Oh, I'm afraid *we won't do /* *we won't have done* them by then – call in on Friday.

d   What's your decision on the takeover deal?
Can you give me until tomorrow? By then *I'll have /* *I'll have had* more time to think about it and *I'll give / I'll have given* you my decision.

e   I can't wait until July! *I won't have / I won't have had* a break since Christmas, so *I'll really need / I'll really have needed* a holiday.

Perfect tenses in the past, present and future

4 **a)** Match a sentence from column A with one from column B to make a dialogue.

A

1 Oh dear, I think I *'ve* .... broken your video.

2 You look slimmer than last time I saw you.

3 How long .... you had your car?

4 Shall I phone back at 11?

5 When .... finished dinner?

6 You were in a bad mood yesterday.

7 .... you seen Mrs Jones this morning?

8 Here are your glasses.

B

a Yes, I .... slept well the night before.

b Oh thank you, I thought I .... lost them.

c Let's have a look.

d Thanks, I .... lost 6 kilos.

e No, she won't be in till this afternoon.

f For about five years, and it's still very reliable.

g Mm, the meeting .... finished by then. Try at 12.

h Probably by about 8.30, so you could phone then.

b) Complete each gap with the appropriate form of *have*, e.g. *'s, 'll have, 'd*, etc.

Pronunciation

Contractions and weak forms

5 **a)** 🔊 Listen and repeat.

I've	I've lost	
I haven't	I haven't heard	
I'd	I'd lost them	
I hadn't	I hadn't slept	
You'll	You'll have /jʊləv/	You'll have done it
Won't	Won't have /wəʊntəv/	Won't have finished

b) 🔊 Listen to the dialogues above and try to read the answers in column B at the same time as the cassette.

c) 🔊 Listen and repeat these questions.

Have you
  /həvjʊ/
Have you seen
Have you seen Mrs Jones?

How long
How long have
  /haʊlɒŋəv/
How long have you had ...?

Had you
  /hədʒʊ/
Had you met ...?

d) 🔊 Listen and write the questions you hear.

1 *How long have you known her* .... ? (6 words)

2 .... ? (7 words)

3 .... ? (6 words)

4 .... ? (8 words)

5 .... ? (6 words)

6 .... ? (5 words)

e) 🔊 Say the questions at the same time as the cassette.

Present Perfect Simple or Continuous

6 Complete the gaps with the best form of the verb in brackets. Remember to use contractions.

A computer help line

1 I *'ve been working*......... (work) all morning on a document and I .... (only / manage) to print two pages of it.

2 I .... (make) some back-up disks and I think I .... (lose) one of my files.

An English student

3 I'm fed up. This is the third time I .... (fail) the First Certificate Exam and I .... (study) here for three years now.

4 I .... (look) for an English–Polish dictionary in the library, but I .... (only / find) a 1965 edition. The librarian said I should talk to you.

A radio phone-in programme about health

5 I feel terrible. I .... (wake up) at 5 a.m. for the last month. I .... (try) two different kinds of sleeping pill, but they just make me feel worse.

6 My husband .... (behave) strangely recently. He .... (start) talking to himself and he .... (stop) going out with his friends. What do you think's wrong with him?

Grammar snack

Just, still, by, so far and perfect tenses

LOOK!

just is used with all perfect tenses, to mean 'a short time before'.
just always comes after *have*.

- I've *just* finished breakfast.
- Mr Doyle had *just* gone when we arrived.
- We'll have *just* started the meeting then.

still is used with all perfect tenses in the negative to add emphasis.
still always comes before any auxiliary verbs.

- Susan *still* hasn't given me back my CD.
- After an hour, the ambulance *still* hadn't come.
- The builders *still* won't have finished by Friday.

by is used with the Past Perfect and Future Perfect and means something happened or will happen 'before a certain time'.
so far is used with the Present Perfect and means 'until now'. It goes at the beginning or end of a sentence.

- **By** | Saturday Stephen had reached Moscow.
  | then Zena will have made the dress.
- **(So far)** we've sent out 100 invitations **(so far)**.

7 **a)** Put *just, still, by* or *so far* into these sentences.

1 ⟨*By* 1997 our family had lived in Argentina for three years.

2 I'm sorry, but Mr Knowles has gone home.

3 They were lucky because when they got to the station the train hadn't left.

4 I've read three chapters of the book you lent me. It's great!

5 This time next year I hope I'll have found a girlfriend.

6 Even if we come back in an hour, she won't have chosen a dress!

7 We had arrived at the airport when the traffic controllers announced a strike.

8 Tom hasn't sold his bike.

b) Finish these sentences so that they are true for you.

1 I've just ....

2 By 1997 I still hadn't ....

3 By this time next year I'll have ....

4 So far this year, I've ....

Reading

Books

8 **a)** Is this an advertisement for   • a library?   • a book club?   • a book shop?

Heading for the beach this summer? Swapping rush-hour claustrophobia for the joys of sun, sand and screaming babies? If it all gets a bit much, you could always bury your head in the sand, or, bearing in mind the perfect all-over tan, take our advice and bury yourself in a good book. With the huge range and brilliant prices on offer, QPD has the literary cure for any bout of the summertime blues – just look at this amazing introductory offer: choose any of these books from only 50p each (plus a total of £2.25 p&p). Is that a head start, or what?

To introduce you to QPD you can choose any five of the books you see here from only 50p each (plus a total of £2.25 p&p). That's a potential saving of £80 on the recommended retail prices. As a member, you're guaranteed savings of up to as much as 50% on the publisher's price of every title you order.

About every two months you'll receive a copy of our *Review* magazine, with its peerless choice of the best in high-quality paperback reading.

Included in each magazine is the Editor's Choice – the most exciting new titles offered at even greater reductions than usual. Simply say on your order form if you wish to choose an alternative.

You will be offered exclusive QPD paperback editions of selected titles before they are officially published in paperback. Bound in durable matt soft covers, QPD editions are denoted by the red corner flash ◥ and are identical in size and content to the original hardback editions.

For your convenience, your choices will be delivered directly to your front door. The single thing we ask is that you buy at least one book from each *Review* magazine you receive during your membership. That membership lasts for a minimum of six issues. To get the ball rolling, simply fill in the coupon and send it to us. You'll have your books on ten days' approval before you need to pay for them.

Once you're satisfied, you pay for them and your membership begins!

QPD, Swindon, SN99 9XX

Q P D
Quality Paperbacks Direct

To: QPD, FREEPOST, Swindon, SN99 1BB ✂

Enter your codes here ☐ ☐ ☐ ☐ ☐

Mr/Mrs/Miss/Ms _____

Address _____ BLOCK CAPITALS

_____ Postcode _____

Tel. no. (incl. STD code) _____

PLEASE SEND NO MONEY NOW • NO STAMP REQUIRED

Please accept my application and enrol me into **Quality Paperbacks Direct**. I am over 18 years of age. Membership is subject to acceptance. Offer available in the UK only. Please allow 28 days for delivery.

Book offers shown:
- L.A. Confidential, James Ellroy — RRP £7.99, Offer Price 50p (3)
- The Go-Between, L.P. Hartley — RRP £6.99, Offer Price 50p (9)
- Animal Farm, George Orwell — RRP £8.99, Offer Price £1 (14)
- Brave New World, Aldous Huxley — RRP £8.99, Offer Price 50p (8)
- Primary Colors, Anonymous — RRP £7.99, Offer Price 50p (13)
- Cry, the Beloved Country, Alan Paton — RRP £6.99, Offer Price 50p (4)
- On the Beach, Nevil Shute — RRP £5.99, Offer Price 50p (2)
- Sherlock Holmes Short Stories — RRP £6.99, Offer Price 50p (6)
- Four Weddings and a Funeral, Richard Curtis — RRP £7.99, Offer Price 50p (11)
- Round the World in Eighty Days, Jules Verne — RRP £6.99, Offer Price 50p (1)
- Treasure Island, R.L. Stevenson — RRP £7.99, Offer Price 50p (12)
- Longman Dictionary of English Language and Culture — RRP £24.95, Offer Price £3 (7)
- Amistad — RRP £9.99, Offer Price £1 (10)
- The Day of the Jackal, Frederick Forsyth — RRP £5.99, Offer Price 50p (5)
- Pride and Prejudice — RRP £6.99, Offer Price 50p (15)

b) Susan started working for QPD today and she's trying to answer some telephone enquiries, but she makes some mistakes. Tick (✓) the correct answers and correct the others.

1 What's the minimum I can spend on the first order?

£4.75. That's five books at 50p each, plus £2.25 post and packaging. ✓

2 Where do I choose the books from?

From our *Review* magazine.

3 Do I have to buy a book from each *Review* magazine while I'm a member?

No, you don't have to.

4 Can I join for just three months? I'm going abroad after that.

No, you have to join for at least twelve months.

5 Can I change my mind and send books back after I've seen them?

No, once you've received your books, you have to pay for them.

6 Should I send payment for the books with my first order?

Yes, please.

7 Can my friend who lives in France join QPD?

Yes, of course.

8 How long will it take for the books to be delivered?

Up to four weeks.

9 Are all your books fiction, or do you have non-fiction?

No, it's all fiction.

10 What's the most expensive book in this special introductory offer?

Well, there's just one book that costs £3 – *Longman Dictionary of English Language and Culture.*

Improve your writing
Describing a book you have enjoyed

9 a) The three circles below contain useful vocabulary for writing about a book. Match each title to a circle.

- *types of book*
- *adjectives to describe the writer*
- *adjectives to describe the story / book*

1 .... 2 .... 3 ....

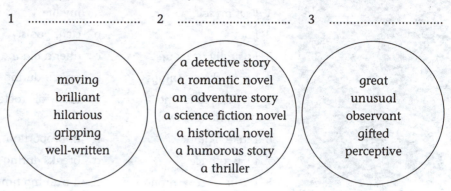

moving
brilliant
hilarious
gripping
well-written

a detective story
a romantic novel
an adventure story
a science fiction novel
a historical novel
a humorous story
a thriller

great
unusual
observant
gifted
perceptive

b) Complete the sentences below about a book you have read recently. Notice that there are three paragraphs: the introduction, the story, and your opinion, and that you need to use the Present Simple for telling the story.

One of the best books I have read recently was .... by ....
It is a .... (**type of book**) and I read it because ....
It is set in .... (**place**), in .... (**time**) and it is about .... (**general topic**).
The story follows the relationship between ... or the events that take place ... or the adventures of ....
At the beginning of the book, ... then, ... , and at the end, ...
I found the book .... and I think .... (**name of author**) is a really .... writer. I'd certainly recommend it to anyone who likes ....

module 6

Vocabulary

1 Here a tennis star is talking about how she copes with major tournaments.
Match the beginnings in column A to the endings in column B.

A		B	
1	I set myself	a	my life.
2	I get	b	clear goals.
3	I usually draw up	c	after a big match.
4	I try to keeps things	d	myself during matches.
5	I try not to let the training take over	e	easily distracted.
6	I take regular	f	in proportion.
7	I try to pace	g	breaks during training.
8	I usually sail through	h	a training timetable and stick to it.
9	I tackle	i	the earlier matches in a tournament.
10	It takes me a few days to wind down	j	difficult matches by thorough mental preparation.

Use and non-use of articles

2 Read these tips from a magazine about finding a good fitness club. Six of
the lines are correct and seven have an article that should not be there. If a
line is correct, put a tick (✓) at the end of it. If there is an article (a / an / the)
that should not be there, circle it.

1 (The) many people go to a gym regularly, to try to

2 lose the weight and cope with the stress of modern life.

3 Here are the some tips for finding the best gym for you.

4 Visit at least three clubs at the time of day you plan to work out.

5 Check for the cleanliness, especially in the changing rooms.

6 Ensure the equipment is well maintained and suited to your

7 requirements. Expect the well qualified, presentable instructors.

8 Check that an instructor is available in the gym area at all times

9 for an assistance. Is the club security-conscious – do you need

10 an ID card to get in? Do you need to pay a membership fee and

11 does the fee include the cost of aerobics classes? Choose a gym

12 a short distance away – if it takes you more than the thirty minutes

13 to get there, you probably won't go.

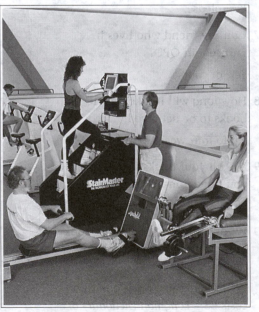

3 In the two texts below, complete the gaps with *a*, *an*, *the* or no article (–).

(A)

Flying problems

Nearly all (1) ....—......... air travellers suffer from (2) .... jet lag to some extent. In (3) .... recent survey, only five per cent said they had never had (4) .... problem. (5) .... most common complaints were (6) .... tiredness and (7) .... disturbed sleep for up to five days after flying.

Here are some tips to help:

• try to book (8) .... morning flight;

• avoid (9) .... alcohol and drink plenty of (10) .... still water;

• get up and walk around (11) .... plane regularly;

• when you get to your destination, try not to sleep during (12) .... next day and go outside as much as possible.

(B)

Depression

(1) .... Canadian study may help to explain why (2) .... women are more likely to suffer from (3) .... depression and (4) .... eating problems than (5) .... men.
(6) .... Canadian study shows that (7) .... women's brains produce around 37 per cent less serotonin, (8) .... important factor in many key brain functions, including (9) .... regulation of (10) .... mood and appetite.

4 Use the prompts to make full sentences. Pay attention to the use of articles and choose the best form of the verb.

a At / Christmas / my mother usually / go / to / church at 8 o'clock, then she / come / home and / cook / huge lunch.
At Christmas my mother usually goes ...
....
....

b Deborah / leave / home / last year – now she / work / as / lecturer in / Vancouver.
....
....

c I / visit / Uncle Frank in / hospital / yesterday morning. He / be / very lucky, because he / have / got one of / best heart specialists in / UK.
....
....
....

d Be / Jamie happy at / school?
Yes. He / like / teachers, and / school / be only / five minutes away, in / Kilmorie Road.
....
....
....

e Gordon / be / terrible cook. He / invite / us for / dinner / last Saturday evening and it / be / one of / worst meals / I / ever / have.
....
....
....

Reading

Self-help books

5 a) Can a book help you to increase your motivation at work? Read this article about self-help books. What is the writer's answer to the question:

Do they work?

a   No, they're a complete waste of money.

b   Yes, they've got some great ideas.

c   They've got some interesting ideas, but they are disappointing in practice.

Self-help books...

Do they work?

Emma Young puts the gurus to the test to see if you can get motivation out of a book.

① Jumping in with Christine Ingham's *101 Ways to Motivate Yourself*, I start with the easy stuff: don't slump, get plenty of rest, listen to your daydreams. So far, so good ...

② Now I'm ready to get motivated. Under the heading *Psyche me up Scotty*, she suggests giving yourself a pep talk. You're supposed to imagine you're a boss who's psyching up some employees. Make it upbeat, she says; think of words that would act like magic. The next step is to make a recording of the speech and play it back to yourself in front of the mirror every morning. I try it. Does it make me feel motivated? No, it makes me feel completely stupid.

③ Time for another tip. Apparently, if you're sick of your job, it helps to get mad. So go on: Shout at your bosses! Scream at the monitor! Ingham reckons the sudden anger release might propel you into action. But unless you do it all inside your head – which appears to make things worse – it's probably more likely to lose you your job.

④ This isn't getting me far, so I try the most scientific-sounding tip in the book: plotting a chart of cumulative progress. I've got a piece to write about motivation and a few days to do it. When you don't feel you're getting anywhere with a task, Ingham suggests drawing up a graph to plot what you've achieved each day. It'll show you that you're making progress and help with motivation, she says. I spend half a day drawing a beautiful graph, and achieve far less than I'd hoped (apart from drawing a beautiful graph).

⑤ Perhaps it's about time I swapped books. Gael Lindenfield's *Self Motivation* demands even more of your time. She tells you what successful self-motivators do. Apparently they love to act, but they also organise, they ask for criticism and they think hard. She describes exercises to help you work this way. But for my money, there's too much to remember and too much to do. Self-help books can only take you so far, and Brits will probably squirm at the American-style advice. Still, you might find the odd tip that's worth a go.

b) Match each of the pictures below to a paragraph in the article. Write the number of the paragraph in the space below.

c) Match the expressions in **bold** from the text in column A with a synonym in column B.

	A		B
1	give yourself a **pep talk**	a	angry
2	**psyching up** some employees	b	occasional
3	make it **upbeat**	c	short, encouraging speech
4	**sick of** your job	d	making (someone) feel confident
5	to get **mad**	e	fed up with
6	I **swapped** books	f	in my opinion
7	But, **for my money**	g	cheerful and positive
8	the **odd** tip	h	changed

Improve your writing

Taking notes: abbreviations

6 **a)** Find an abbreviation in the box for each of the words and phrases below.

re.	a.m.	Sat.	N.B.	i.e.	p.m.	a.s.a.p.	inc.	
etc.	e.g.	P.S.	&					

1 ....*e.g.*.... for example
2 .... as soon as possible
3 .... and
4 .... etcetera
5 .... Saturday
6 .... this means / which means
7 .... please note
8 .... about
9 .... morning
10 .... afternoon
11 .... including
12 .... postscript (a message written at the end of a letter, after the signature)

b) Complete the gaps in these sentences with an abbreviation.

1 You can put different toppings on your pizza, ...*e.g.*.... cheese, tomato, olives or ham.
2 I had to get up at 6 .... to catch the train.
3 We went to all the famous places – Times Square, Broadway, Central Park, ...
4 Fish .... chips: £3.50.
5 Mrs Lawrence phoned. Please ring back ....
6 The coach leaves on .... at 9.30. You'll need to bring a packed lunch.
7 Mary – please phone your dentist .... your appointment.
8 The film is only open to adults, ... people over eighteen.
9 The CDs cost $40, ... post and packaging.
10 That's all for now, see you soon,
   John
   .... I love you!

Writing notes

LOOK!

When we write notes (such as phone messages) we miss out obvious words and use dashes (–) and abbreviations:

• *Your mum rang at 11.30. She's still expecting you this weekend. She's out on Saturday morning from 9 to 11 and she'll leave the key with Mrs Benson next door.*
• *11.30 – your mum rang – still expecting you this weekend. Out Sat a.m. 9 – 11 – will leave key with Mrs Benson next door.*

We miss out:
• pronouns (*he, she, it* etc.)
• auxiliary verbs (*'s* etc.)
• verb *to be* (*'s*)
• prepositions (*on, in, at* etc.)
• articles (*the, a / an*)

7 Change these full messages into shorter notes. In each case try to use approximately the number of words in the brackets (   ). A contraction = 2 words, an abbreviation or time = 1 word.

a Paul phoned at 6.00. He wants to know if you're coming to Anne's party on Saturday. Please ring him back as soon as possible.
   6.00 – Paul phoned. Wants to know if ....
   ....
   (about 15 words)

b Mr Larsen phoned at 10.30. His plane is arriving at 9 o'clock, not 8 o'clock on Thursday morning.
   ....
   ....
   (about 11 words)

c I've gone to the gym. Autoclinic phoned about the car. It will be ready tomorrow afternoon.
   ....
   ....
   (about 12 words)

d Susie phoned at 3.00. She's going to see *Godzilla* tonight with Paul. They'll meet you in Shades wine bar at 7.00.
   ....
   ....
   (about 15 words)

Different ways of emphasising things

8 **a)** Make this script for a soap opera more dramatic by adding the words from the box in a suitable place. Keep the words **in this order**:

Drew enters the flat, to see Jenny looking very upset. The noise of plates smashing, and screaming can be heard coming from the kitchen.

JENNY: Oh Drew, I'm *so* pleased to see you ...

DREW: Why? What's all that shouting in the kitchen?

JENNY: It's Simon – he's gone mad, because he thinks

Anna's seeing someone else.

DREW: (*walking towards the kitchen*) Right, I'm going to

stop this ...

JENNY: (*running after him and pulling him back*) No, it's

dangerous! He's got a knife!

DREW: You don't think he'll use it do you?

JENNY: I think he might, because he's been drinking ...

Anna's terrified.

DREW: (*walking around agitatedly*) This is ridiculous ...

let's try and talk to him.

JENNY: It won't do any good, he's drunk.

DREW: (*picking up the phone*) Okay then, let's call the

police – there's nothing else we can do.

Anna and Simon

Jenny and Drew

so on earth completely far too really do absolutely far too absolutely

b) 🔊 Listen to some phrases from the dialogue and mark the words which carry the main stress on the script above.

c) 🔊 Now listen to the complete dialogue and say it at the same time.

Emphatic constructions with *what* and *it* (cleft sentences)

LOOK!

Remember how we can change the word order to emphasise a certain part of a sentence:

- *Her terrible accent annoyed me most.*
- ***What annoyed me most was** her terrible accent.*
- *Mike left all the windows open.*
- ***It was Mike who** left all the windows open.*

9 **a)** Put these sentences into the correct order, using cleft sentences. The first word is underlined.

1 grandmother – gave – was – who – awful – It – that – my – me – picture

   It was my grandmother who gave me that awful picture .

2 like – hot – What – a – bath – feel – is – nice – I – really

   ....
   ....

3 It – crashed – me – car – who – the – wasn't

   ....
   ....

4 designs – I've – are – latest – got – our – What – here

   ....
   ....

5 who – play – through – It – slept – the – was – all – you

   ....
   ....

6 who – was – 1998 – It – won – World Cup – France – the – in

   ....
   ....

7 about – impressed – was – enthusiasm – me – his – What – Sam

   ....
   ....

b) Change these sentences to give more emphasis, using *What* and *It*.

1 I hate living here because of the pollution.

   What I hate about living here is the pollution .

2 I love Autumn because of the colour of the leaves.

   What ....

3 John didn't pay for the wedding ring, Sarah did.

   It ....

4 You need a new car.

   What ....

5 Did you choose the furniture?

   Was ....

6 I don't understand how my sister paid for three holidays this year.

   What ....

Pronunciation

Cleft sentences

LOOK!

In this type of sentence, we often stress the verb in the *What* clause.

- *What I like about Madrid is the nightlife.*
- *What I hate about cooking is the washing up.*
- *What annoys me about him is his laziness.*
- *What interests me most about languages is how different they are.*

10 **a)** Listen to the sentences above and try to say them at the same time, paying attention to the rhythm.

b) Complete these sentences so that they are true for you, then practise saying them with the correct rhythm.

1 What I like about .... is ....
   ....

2 What I hate about .... is ....
   ....

3 What annoys me about .... is ....
   ....

4 What interests me most about .... is ....
   ....
   ....

41

module 7

Vocabulary

Word building

1 **a)** Complete the charts with the correct form of the word

	Verb	Noun	Adjective
1	decorate	*decoration*	*decorative*
2	....	origin	....
3	....	....	celebratory
4	commemorate	....	....
5	....	....	participatory
6	....	fascination	....
7	demonstrate	....	....

	Noun	Adjective	Adverb
8	tradition	....	....
9	....	....	historically
10	————	....	internationally
11	commerce	....	....
12	....	atmospheric	....

b) Complete the gaps with a word from the tables above.

1 People of all ages *participate* .... in the dancing.

2 We had a .... drink when we heard that Jim had passed his final exam.

3 The flamenco musicians who play during the festival are .... famous.

4 There's no .... evidence to show that St. Nicholas ever existed.

5 Many people feel that Christmas has become too .... nowadays.

6 Every November there's a ceremony to .... the dead of the two World Wars.

7 At Christmas many people .... their Christmas trees.

8 The music during the play was really .... – beautiful and mysterious.

9 People laid thousands of flowers outside Kensington Palace as a .... of their love for Princess Diana.

Pronunciation

Adverbs

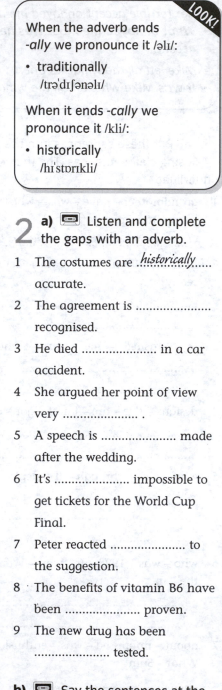

LOOK!

When the adverb ends -*ally* we pronounce it /əlɪ/:

• traditionally /trəˈdɪʃənəlɪ/

When it ends -*cally* we pronounce it /klɪ/:

• historically /hɪˈstɒrɪkli/

2 **a)** 🖭 Listen and complete the gaps with an adverb.

1 The costumes are *historically* .... accurate.

2 The agreement is .... recognised.

3 He died .... in a car accident.

4 She argued her point of view very ....

5 A speech is .... made after the wedding.

6 It's .... impossible to get tickets for the World Cup Final.

7 Peter reacted .... to the suggestion.

8 The benefits of vitamin B6 have been .... proven.

9 The new drug has been .... tested.

b) 🖭 Say the sentences at the same time as the tape, paying particular attention to the pronunciation of -*ally*.

Grammar check-up

Relative pronouns

3 **a)** In the questions below which relative pronouns (*who, which, that, whose, when, where*) can go in the gaps?

> ## What do you call ...

1 a person ....*who / that*.... you can depend on?

2 a very small living thing .... causes infectious illnesses?

3 a person .... work is the most important thing in their life and .... does not have time for anything else?

4 a snack .... you often eat in the cinema, made from corn?

5 a small room .... people are held overnight in a police station?

6 the day in November .... American people celebrate the origins of their country?

7 a piece of equipment .... you can put a video camera on, and .... has got three legs?

8 a small insect .... body is red with black spots?

b) Write the answers to the questions above.

1 *Dependable* ....

2 ....

3 ....

4 ....

5 ....

6 ....

7 ....

8 ....

c) In three of the sentences above you can leave out the relative pronoun.

Which are they?

....

....

Why?

....

....

Listen and read

Hughie Erskine is a charming and attractive young man. Unfortunately, however, he has not been very successful in business and therefore never has any money.

Read and / or listen to this extract from *The Model Millionaire* by Oscar Wilde.

4 **a)** Find three mistakes in this picture of the scene described in the extract.

b) Are these sentences *T* (true) or *F* (false)?

1 Trevor likes people who aren't very intelligent because it is easy to have a conversation with them. .....*T*......

2 Hughie doesn't need an invitation to come and visit Trevor. ....

3 The portrait of the beggar was quite small. ....

4 Trevor saw Hughie give the beggar some money. ....

5 Hughie felt embarrassed about his moment of generosity. ....

One morning, Hughie called in to see a great friend of his, Alan Trevor. Trevor was a painter. He had been much attracted by Hughie at first, it must be admitted, just because of his personal charm. 'The only people a painter should know,' he used to say, 'are
5   people who are both beautiful and stupid, people who are a pleasure to look at and restful to talk to.' But after he got to know Hughie better, he liked him quite as much for his bright, cheerful spirits, and his generous, carefree nature, and had asked him to visit whenever he liked.

10   When Hughie came in, he found Trevor putting the finishing touches to a wonderful life-size picture of a beggar. The beggar himself was standing on a raised platform in a corner of the room. He was a tired old man with a lined face and a sad expression. Over his shoulder was thrown a rough brown coat, all torn and full of
15   holes; his thick boots were old and mended, and with one hand he leant on a rough stick, while with the other he held out his old hat for money.

'What an astonishing model!' whispered Hughie, as he shook hands with his friend.

20   'An astonishing model?' shouted Trevor at the top of his voice; 'I should think so! Such beggars are not met with every day. Good heavens!'

'Poor old man!' said Hughie. 'How miserable he looks! But I suppose, to you painters, his face is his fortune.'

25   'Certainly,' replied Trevor, 'you don't want a beggar to look happy, do you?'

After some time the servant came in, and told Trevor that the frame maker wanted to speak to him.

The old beggar took advantage of Trevor's absence to rest for a
30   moment. He looked so miserable that Hughie pitied him, and felt in his pockets to see what money he had. All he could find was a pound and some pennies. 'Poor old man!' he thought, 'he needs it more than I do, but I shan't have much money myself for a week or two'; and he walked across the room and slipped the pound into the
35   beggar's hand.

The old man jumped, and a faint smile passed across his old lips. 'Thank you, sir,' he said, 'thank you.'

Then Trevor arrived, and Hughie left, a little red in the face at what he had done.

44

Non-defining relative clauses

5 Read this summary of *The Model Millionaire* by Oscar Wilde.

Hughie Erskine, (1) *who was a handsome but poor young man* , was in love with Laura Merton (2) ....

One day Hughie visited his friend Alan Trevor. Trevor (3) .... was just finishing a portrait of a beggar. 'Poor old man!' thought Hughie, 'he looks so miserable,' and gave the man a pound (4) .... The beggar smiled, 'Thank you, Sir, thank you.' Hughie spent the rest of the day with Laura (5) .... and he had to walk home because he had no money to pay for transport. That night he went to the club (6) .... Trevor told him that the *beggar* was in reality Baron Hausberg (7) .... Hughie felt deeply embarrassed. The following day he received an envelope from the Baron (8) .... Inside was a cheque for £10,000!

The Model Millionaire by Oscar Wilde, from *Outstanding Short Stories*, Longman Fiction.

Add this additional information in the gaps in the story, using non-defining relative clauses. Make sure you include commas where necessary.

- his financial skills had made him a millionaire
- she was rather annoyed because he had given away his last pound
- it was the last bit of money he had
- he was an artist
- her father had demanded £10,000 to allow them to marry
- he was a handsome but poor young man
- it had this message written on the outside: 'a wedding present from an old beggar to Hughie and Laura'
- he met Trevor there

Participle relative clauses

6 Shorten these sentences to make participle relative clauses. Use the Present or Past Participle and cross out unnecessary words.

a Who's that woman who is talking to Mr Pozzi?

b Packages which are left unattended will be taken away.

c Is that your phone which is ringing?

d Anyone who parks here will have to pay a £20 fine.

e All the people who were injured in the accident have been released from hospital.

f The conference which takes place next week could change the future of the company.

g I like Martinis which are shaken, and which are not stirred.

h Most of the people who were invited to the wedding came to it.

Relative clauses

All types

7 In each of the following extracts from an entertainments guide, combine the information to make two longer sentences.

COMEDY

The Comedy Experience finishes on Friday. It features the brilliant Steve Simons and newcomer Martin Jones. Tickets are available on the door. They are priced £8 and £12.

CINEMA

Terminator 2 is an excellent sequel to the original *Terminator*. It stars Arnold Schwarzenegger. This version is a 'must' for all Arnie fans. It includes new special effects.

OUTDOOR CONCERTS

The first concert in Crystal Palace Park features three groups. Their music instantly brings back the atmosphere of the 1970s.

Hot Chocolate will be performing hits like ***You Sexy Thing***. They are the main attraction.

Ⓐ

The Comedy Experience featuring / which features the brilliant Steve Simons and newcomer Martin Jones, finishes on Friday. Tickets ...
....

Ⓑ

Terminator 2 ....
....
....
....
....

Ⓒ

The first concert ....
....
....
....
....

Improve your writing

Punctuation

8 Add all the necessary punctuation (capital letters, commas, apostrophes and quotation marks) to this article.

A woman who ....
....
....
....
....
....
....
....
....
....
....
....
....
....
....
....

Not Too Old

a woman who became britains oldest test-tube mother has attacked critics of her plan to have a second child. christine taylor who told doctors she was forty-eight instead of fifty-five described as stupid people who said she was too old to look after another baby. she said I feel just as energetic as when I had my first baby twenty years ago. she claims that her life with son ralph conceived through fertility treatment in 1997 is just the same as a young mothers. however she is worried that ralph might be embarrassed by his parents age. thats why I want to have another child immediately she explains so hell have someone in the same situation.

mrs Taylor who has advertised locally for an egg donor says she has had a good response.

Quantifiers

9 Complete the gaps in each text with a quantifier from the boxes below. In each case, one of the quantifiers **cannot** be used.

Rollerblades

The best: ☆☆☆☆☆ *Racers*

Super fast and smooth, these skates come in (1) ....*several*........ different colours and have (2) .... extra features, including holes which give (3) .... of ventilation. One small reservation is that there's (4) .... noise when you go at high speed.

The worst: ☆ *Grippers*

These skates take (5) .... time to put on – almost 10 minutes and don't provide (6) .... support to your feet. They come in (7) .... colours – only grey, black or white.

enough   plenty   too much
too many   quite a few
very few   <u>several</u>
slightly too much

Choc 'n' Nut Ice cream

The best: ☆☆☆☆☆ *Naughty and Nutty*

This ice cream has absolutely (1) .... of flavour and should satisfy (2) .... of the chocolate lovers among our readers. There are (3) .... of nuts and not (4) .... sugar.

The worst: ☆ *Nut and Choc*

There are (5) .... nuts in this ice cream, but not many, and (6) .... chocolate. There is also (7) .... sugar. A real disappointment.

too much (x2)   any   loads
plenty   not nearly enough
some   just the right amount

CD Players

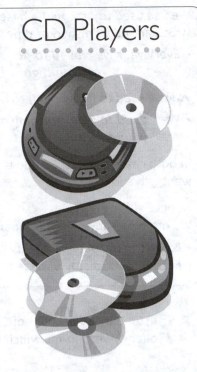

The best: ☆☆☆☆ *Genesis*

We tried (1) .... CDs from pop to classical and (2) .... kind of music sounded superb. There are only (3) .... special features, but these are worthwhile and simple to use. The only problem is that (4) .... shops actually have it in stock.

The worst: ☆ *Horizon*

We didn't think (5) .... of the CDs played well. It looks quite futuristic but there are (6) .... buttons and flashing lights for our liking.

any (x2)   various   too many
a few   plenty   very few

Grammar snack

Used to / would + verb

> **LOOK!**
>
> We use *used to* or *would* + base form to talk about **past habits** which are now finished or different.
>
> - Every year we | **used to go** / **would go** | to Spain for our holidays.
>
> We use *used to* (not *would*) to talk about **past states** or **situations**.
>
> - We | **used to love** / ~~would love~~ | playing on the beach.
>
> In both cases the Past Simple is always possible (*Every year we went... We loved...*)
>
> Notice:
> We often use adverbs of frequency after *would* and before *used to*:
>
> - I'd **often** stay outside all day.
> - I **often** used to stay outside all day.

10 **a)** In Carrie's account of Christmas when she was young, cross out any verb forms which are not possible.

The night before Christmas (1) **we'd always go** / **we always used to go** / **we always went** to Midnight Mass. (2) **We'd love** / **We used to love** / **We loved** this because it meant staying up late. The next morning (3) **we'd wake up** / **we used to wake up** / **we woke up** very early and (4) **we'd open** / **we used to open** / **we opened** our stockings which were hung outside the door. (5) **We'd live** / **We used to live** / **We lived** in a house with a chimney, and (6) **I'd believe** / **I used to believe** / **I believed** that Father Christmas came down it with my presents. (7) **We'd usually have** / **We usually used to have** / **We usually had** a huge Christmas lunch of turkey and Christmas pudding. I remember the Christmases (8) **I'd spend** / **I used to spend** / **I spent** in Italy, when (9) **we'd drink** / **we used to drink** / **we drank** Martinis on the beach before Christmas lunch – and no turkey – (10) **instead we'd have** / **we used to have** / **we had** pasta and salad. It just wasn't the same.

b) Put these sentences in the correct order. The first word is underlined.

1 get – at – <u>I</u> – of – Christmas – used – always – to – lots – presents

   I always used to get lots of
   presents at Christmas .

2 always – until – New Year's Eve – up – midnight – 'd – <u>On</u> – stay – we

   ....
   ....
   ....
   ....

3 used – our – <u>We</u> – go – holidays – never – for – to – abroad

   ....
   ....
   ....
   ....

4 day – to – was – I – used – most – day – <u>The</u> – enjoy – Christmas

   ....
   ....
   ....
   ....

c) Change the sentences above so that they are true for you.

1 I always used to get lots of
   presents *on my name day* .

2 ....
   ....
   ....
   ....

3 ....
   ....
   ....
   ....

4 ....
   ....
   ....
   ....

module 8

Dictionary work

Word combinations: politics

1 a) Here are some common word combinations. Use the extracts from the *Longman Essential Activator* to complete the diagrams on the right.

> **campaign** /kæmˈpeɪn/ [v I] to do things, such as writing to the government and organising public meetings, because you want to change society or stop something bad from happening
> **+ against** *Greenpeace campaigned against nuclear weapons tests in the Pacific.*
> **+ for** *Disabled people have been campaigning for equal right for years.*
> **campaign to do something** *The animal rights movement is campaigning to stop experiments on live animals.*
>
> **economic** /ˌekəˈnɒmɪk, ˌiː-‖-ˈnɑː-/ [adj usually before noun] use this about the way that a country's money and wealth is produced, spent and controlled: *The President's economic reforms have put a lot of people out of work.* | *a period of economic growth* | *the need for economic planning*
>
> **issue** /ˈɪʃuː, ˈɪsjuː‖ˈɪʃuː/ [n C] an important subject that people discuss and argue about: *The control of nuclear weapons is an important issue.*
> **+ of** *the issue of drugs in sports*
> **political / environmental / educational etc issues** *a book dealing with environmental issues*
> **major / big / key issue** (= a very important issue) *Unemployment and crime were the key issues in the election campaign.*
>
> **political** /pəˈlɪtɪkəl/ [adj usually before noun] connected with the government of a country or local area: *There are two main political parties in the US.* | *the British political system* | *She began her political career as a city councillor.*
>
> **politics** /ˈpɒlɪtɪks‖ˈpɑː-/ [n U] activities and ideas that are connected with governing a country or local area: *Gun control is one of the biggest issues in American politics at the moment.* | *Many young people aren't interested in politics.*
> **party politics** (= when political parties are trying to get an advantage over each other)
> **local politics** (= politics in a town or city) *She's always been deeply involved in local politics.*

b) Complete the gaps with one of the key words above. Try not to look back at the diagrams.

1 The key *issue* in the next election will be unemployment.

2 The worsening .... situation in Asia meant many people lost their jobs.

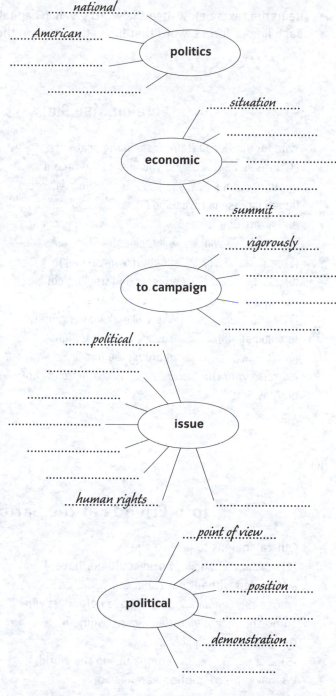

3 I'm very involved in local ....

4 The 1950s saw a period of .... growth in the UK.

5 Rachel Littlestone left teaching to pursue a .... career.

6 The President discussed the .... of human rights during his visit.

7 We intend to .... vigorously against the building of the new ring road.

Vocabulary

Word building

2 Read the texts below. Use the word given in capitals at the end of each line to form a word that fits in the space in the same line.

Ⓐ

Vote on May 9th!

Vote for the Social Democrats in the next
(1) ....._election_..... ! If you look at the record   ELECT
of our present (2) .... , you will see a   GOVERN
huge increase in taxes and (3) .... ,   EMPLOY
and a rate of (4) .... which is out of   INFLATE
control. If we win, we will tackle the
(5) .... situation by investing in   ECONOMY
(6) .... projects and training courses   EDUCATE
to help our young people become better
(7) .... We will make it our priority   QUALIFY
to eliminate (8) .... and to fight   BUREAUCRAT
(9) .... wherever we find it. So,   CORRUPT
exercise your (10) .... right and vote   DEMOCRAT
on May 9th!

Ⓑ

Join Friends of the Earth

Our campaigns to protect the
(1) .... world could not have   NATURE
succeeded without our (2) .... ,   SUPPORT
whose (3) .... have helped us win   CONTRIBUTE
some significant victories against some of
the most (4) ....   POWER
(5) .... companies in the world.   INDUSTRY
We have raised public awareness of
(6) .... issues in general, and   ENVIRONMENT
recently we have (7) .... to make   CAMPAIGN
the use of ozone-destroying CFCs
(8) .... Join us now and help us   LAW
find alternative (9) .... to world   SOLVE
problems, and make our (10) ....   POLITICS
sit up and listen.

Pronunciation

Word stress and reading aloud

3 a) 📼 Listen to these pairs of words or say them to yourself, and mark the main stress on each.

●

economy	economic
nature	natural
educate	education
contribute	contribution
qualify	qualification
industry	industrial
bureaucrat	bureaucracy
environment	environmental
democrat	democracy
politics	politician

b) 📼 Try to say the words at the same time as the cassette.

c) 📼 Read the two texts in exercise 2 at the same time as the cassette, paying attention to the stress and weak forms.

Grammar check-up

Infinitive of purpose

4 Match the first line of each joke in column A with the second line in column B.

	A		B
1	Why did the elephant paint his toe-nails red?	a	To hide in the cherry trees.
2	Why did the egg go to the jungle?	b	To bury her dead batteries.
3	Why did the girl dig a hole for her radio?	c	To be an eggsplorer.
4	Why did the elephant wear sunglasses on the beach?	d	To get to the other side.
5	Why did you hang the picture of me in the cellar?	e	To avoid being recognised.
6	Why did the chicken cross the road?	f	To frighten all the mice.

Answer these questions about yourself, using an infinitive of purpose.

1 When did you last go to the hairdresser's, and why?
Three weeks ago, to have my hair cut and coloured ....

2 When did you last go to hospital, and why?
....

3 When did you last phone a friend, and why?
....

4 When did you last go to a sports centre, and why?
....

5 When did you last write a letter, and why?
....

Infinitive forms

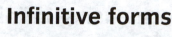

5 Complete the second sentence so that it has a similar meaning to the first one, using an infinitive form in the present or past (with or without *to*).

a We said you shouldn't drive so fast.
We told you *not to drive so fast* .

b I really don't want to talk about it, if you don't mind.
I'd rather ....
....

c I don't know why you didn't bring your photos to show me.
You should ....
....

d I advise you to get some sleep – you've got a long day tomorrow.
You'd better ....
....

e I think Maria's English is improving.
Maria's English seems ....
....

f Sonia felt very depressed because of the film.
The film made Sonia ....
....

g People think Picasso painted this picture.
Picasso is thought ....
....

Patterns using infinitives with *to*

6 Complete the gaps with a word from the box.

> tend an effort manage a chance what
> something sorry afraid late pretended

1 We were *sorry* .... to hear about the accident.

2 If you had .... to work in another country, would you take it?

3 Did you .... to persuade Laszlo to come?

4 It's too .... to change your mind now.

5 Amazing! I really don't know .... to say!

6 Girls .... to be tidier than boys.

7 I know you don't like Lucia, but you could have made .... to be polite.

8 Jo .... to be asleep when Frank rang.

9 Shall we have .... to eat before the film?

10 Mrs Bixby was .... to ask the price of the coat, because it looked so expensive.

Infinitive or gerund (*-ing* form)

7 Underline the correct form of the verb in the text.

The Prime Minister was asked today how he plans (1) *deal with* / *to deal with* / *dealing with* growing crime amongst teenagers. He believes that it is important (2) *create* / *to create* / *creating* more jobs and (3) *provide* / *to provide* / *providing* more opportunities for them (4) *get* / *to get* / *getting* work. At the same time he thinks that young criminals should (5) *be sent* / *to be sent* / *be sending* to prison for longer. 'The Labour Government is tough on crime', is his party's slogan. Parents must continue (6) *play* / *to play* / *playing* a vital role in (7) *help* / *to help* / *helping* the Government (8) *make* / *to make* / *making* our streets safer. The Government is also considering (9) *introduce* / *to introduce* / *introducing* a curfew in some city centres (10) *stop* / *to stop* / *stopping* young people being out on the streets after 11 o'clock, when most serious crimes happen.

Reading

8 **a)** What are the customs for giving tips in your country? How much money would you give to:

a waiter? ....

a hairdresser? ....

a taxi driver? ....

b) Complete the gap in the following sentences with the correct form (infinitive, with or without *to*, or in the passive, or gerund) of the verb in brackets.

1 In France, it is always worth *carrying* .... (carry) a few francs for tips to taxi drivers, and it is customary .... (give) a couple of francs to the cinema usher who shows you to your seat.

2 In the United States, it is not uncommon .... (chase) out of a restaurant by waiters if you fail .... (leave) a tip.

3 Life gets tricky in Japan, where people are expected .... (show) gratitude, rather than actually hand over money.

4 When .... (tip) and how much have always been tricky questions for the British.

5 In Asia, you may .... (ask) for a tip in the most unusual situations, so it is advisable .... (carry) small amounts of money in your pockets, ... (make) life easier.

6 And finally, what are visitors to the UK advised .... (do)?

7 Should tips .... (include) in the minimum wage?

8 Holidays in the Middle East can .... (get) very expensive, where tipping is expected by nearly everyone.

9 Travellers to Scandinavia may .... (be) relieved to find, given the high cost of living, that tipping is not expected.

10 The report also angered waiters, waitresses and hairdressers by .... (suggest) that tips should .... (include) in the minimum hourly rate.

c) The sentences in exercise 8b have been removed from this article about tipping. Decide where the sentences go in the text. There is **one sentence which you do not need to use**.

Some handy tips about tipping

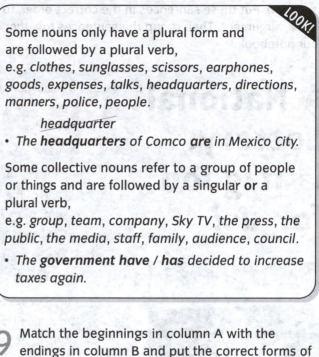

The low pay debate highlights the practice that varies widely

a ....7......
This was the question being fiercely debated when the Government and unions clashed over the Low Pay Commission's report this week. The report suggests a minimum wage of £3.60 an hour, disappointing unions, which are campaigning for £4.61.

b ....
This will particularly affect those who work in restaurants where a service charge is included in the bill.

c ....
These issues are all the more topical because millions will soon be setting off on summer holidays to countries where customs vary widely. Here are some general guidelines on what to do.

d ....
The advice I was given by an American friend was: 'If in doubt, leave a tip.' This is a general rule of thumb. At a bar, for example, staff will expect you to leave them the change.

e ....
However, French law requires that restaurants, cafes and hotel bills include the service charge, usually 10–15 per cent, so a tip is not expected.

f ....
For the more penny-pinching traveller, try Yemen, the only country in the region without a strong tipping culture.

g ....
There can be a serious loss of face for the people involved, such as waiters, if you try to insist on giving them a tip.

h ....
Hairdressers and people who work in restaurants will probably think you are mad if you try to leave a tip.

i ....
The popular travel guide *The Lonely Planet* has these suggestions. You should tip 10–15 per cent of the total bill in a restaurant and round up taxi fares to the nearest 50p.

Grammar snack
Plural nouns and collective nouns

LOOK!

Some nouns only have a plural form and are followed by a plural verb,
e.g. *clothes, sunglasses, scissors, earphones, goods, expenses, talks, headquarters, directions, manners, police, people.*

~~headquarter~~
• The **headquarters** of Comco **are** in Mexico City.

Some collective nouns refer to a group of people or things and are followed by a singular **or** a plural verb,
e.g. *group, team, company, Sky TV, the press, the public, the media, staff, family, audience, council.*

• The **government have / has** decided to increase taxes again.

9 Match the beginnings in column A with the endings in column B and put the correct forms of *have, be,* or *do* in the boxes (often there is more than one possibility).

A

1 The police in England   *don't*

2 The audience still

3 My family

4 Your expenses

5 The press

6 Electrical goods

7 Independent TV

8 The talks in Geneva

B

a showing *Terminator 2* tonight.

b allowed into the church.

c continued throughout the day.

d usually carry guns.

e selling very well this year.

f ridiculously high!

g celebrate birthdays any more.

h stopped clapping.

Improve your writing

Writing an argument for and against

10 **a)** Put these sentences in the correct order, to make a logical argument. Then group the sentences together in paragraphs in your notebook.

A National Lottery: is it good for us?

.... In addition to this, it encourages people to pin all their hopes on their dream of 'a big win', instead of dealing with the day-to-day problems of real life.

.... Another key point is the huge amount of enjoyment that thousands of 'hopefuls' get from participating.

.... One of the strongest arguments for having a national lottery is that large sums of money can be given to good causes, such as sports facilities for the handicapped.

......*1*...... Many people have mixed feelings about having a national lottery in their country.

.... In conclusion, I think it is difficult to see a clear-cut answer to this question because there are so many factors to take into account, and it probably depends on your age, experience, and beliefs.

.... Furthermore, money can be used for the arts, for example by building new museums or redecorating theatres.

.... Thirty years ago in the United Kingdom the Government were against the idea, whereas nowadays people win millions of pounds every week.

.... One other important consideration is the enormous profits that the lottery companies make, in relation to the money they give away.

.... On the other hand, many people are concerned about the possible negative effects of the lottery.

.... What's more, these are often the kind of charitable projects which otherwise would not receive much funding from the Government.

b) Choose the correct alternative in these sentences.

1 I'm in favour of the pay rise *although* / *despite* it'll cost the company a lot of money.

2 If you're single, you have a lot of independence. *On the other hand* / *What's more*, you can get lonely.

3 Banning cars in city centres would certainly reduce pollution. *Whereas* / *Furthermore*, people might get more exercise.

4 *In conclusion* / *Another key point is* the danger of people relying on machines to think for them.

5 Politicians face a lot of criticism. *In addition to this* / *However*, they can have a significant influence on people's lives.

6 *One of the strongest arguments for* / *People have very strong views on* the death penalty is that it discourages serious crime.

module 9

Vocabulary

Describing things that are odd or unusual

1 **a)** Put a word from the box under each picture.

> broken down   melted   inside out   a crack   a mark   upside down
> scratched   torn   got stuck   chipped   a hole   the wrong size

b) Put the words and phrases from the box in the correct space in the table below.

It's (is)	stained
	cracked
	(1) *chipped*
	(2) ....
	(3) ....
	on the wrong side
	in the wrong place
	going the wrong way
	(4) ....
	(5) ....
	(6) ....

It's (has)	been damaged
	(7) ....
	(8) ....
	(9) ....

It's got (has)	a tear	
	(10)	in it
	(11)	
	a stain	
	a scratch	on it
	(12)	

1. *chipped*

LOOK!

We often use *bad / badly* and *slight / slightly* to show how much something is damaged:

		adjectives
• *It's **slightly***		*torn*
	badly	*cracked*
		chipped

Notice: with *broken* and *melted*, we use *completely* not *badly*:

• *It's **completely***		*broken*
		melted

		nouns
• *It's got a **slight***		*tear*
	bad	*crack*
		stain
		mark

55

c) Complete the gaps with a suitable word from exercise 1b.

1 Janet dropped her Walkman while she was getting off the bus and now it's completely _broken_ .

2 This dress is reduced because it's got a slight .... on it.

3 It's fashionable to wear jeans that are .... around the knees.

4 This carpet's got a really bad .... where Magda spilt some wine on it.

5 Don't use that egg – it's got a .... in it.

6 I can't open this bag – the zip's got ....

7 You're going the wrong .... if you want to get to the hospital.

Pronunciation

Consonant clusters

> LOOK!
>
> When you find it difficult to pronounce two or more consonants together, try starting with the last one.
> 🔊 Listen to this example or say it aloud.
> *cracked* /t – kt – ækt – rækt – krækt/

2 a) 🔊 Listen to these words and say them aloud.

cracked	chipped	over-cooked
/krækt/	/tʃɪpt/	/əʊvəˈkʊkt/
scratched	stained	damaged
/skrætʃt/	/steɪnd/	/ˈdæmɪdʒd/

b) 🔊 Here are some common consonant clusters. Listen to these groups of words and repeat them.

/skr/	/spr/	/spl/	/str/
scratch	spring	split	stress
describe	expression	explain	strong
tapescript	aspirin	explode	string
ice cream	sprained	explore	extremely

Modal verbs

Revision

3 In each of the following sentences correct the modal in **bold**. In most cases there is more than one possibility.

could / can

a If you like, I **may** make an appointment for you to see Dr Singh tomorrow.

b Passengers **don't have to** smoke while the plane is taking off.

c Don't let Sylvie climb that tree. She **can** fall.

d You probably **mustn't** keep your keys in that pocket because they could easily be stolen.

e I'm afraid Karen **couldn't** come to the party tomorrow because she's not feeling very well.

f Oh no! It **mustn't** be six o'clock already! I feel like I've had no sleep at all!

g Be careful! That pot's very heavy. You **should** drop it.

h I absolutely **ought to** get up at seven o'clock because the train leaves at eight.

4 Complete the gaps in these conversations with an appropriate modal verb.

a Is it possible to do colour copies on this printer?
Well you _can / could_ , but it takes ages.

b Do you think it'll snow tonight?
It .... It's suddenly got very cold.

c Don't you think you'd better see someone about your toothache?
I know I .... , but I hate going to the dentist.

d Isn't that your boyfriend over there with Susie?
It .... be! He's supposed to be in Paris on business!

e Do I really need to speak Spanish for the job?
Well, you ...., but it helps.

f Are the car keys in your jacket pocket?
Well, they .... be, unless someone's taken them.

g Come inside now – it's getting dark!
Oh .... we? We're in the middle of a game.

Past modals

5 Vanessa, Georgina, Mike, Hannah and Gavin are students who share a student house. They often have arguments. Complete each gap with one of these past forms of the modal verbs *should*, *ought to*, *must*, *can't*, *might*, or *could*, and an appropriate verb.

VANESSA: Someone forgot to lock the front door last night.

MIKE: Well, it (a) *can't have been* me. I definitely remember locking it, so it (b) .... someone who came home after me.

GEORGINA: You slept in the garden all night! Why didn't you wake us up?

GAVIN: Well, I rang the bell for ages, but no one answered. You (c) .... to bed.

GEORGINA: Oh, you idiot. You (d) .... a stone at the window.

GEORGINA: Vanessa and Gavin aren't speaking to each other this morning.

MIKE: They (e) .... an argument. I remember hearing shouting last night.

VANESSA: Who's this?

MIKE: It's just my friend, Bill.

VANESSA: Well, you (f) .... us that you were bringing someone home. I just sat on him!

GEORGINA: Oh no! Where have my chocolates gone? There are only two left!

VANESSA: Well, I think the cat (g) .... them because I forgot to feed him, or it (h) .... Gavin, because you know what he's like when he's hungry!

GAVIN: Look at this, and I left Georgina a note!

MIKE: Well she (i) .... it.

MIKE: You look terrible.

GAVIN: Yes, I feel really sick.

MIKE: Well, you (j) .... Georgina's chocolates. It's your own fault.

Past modals in everyday conversations

6 Use the prompts to make complete sentences in these conversations.

a

PETE: Oh no! I / lose / my wallet.

Oh no! I've lost my wallet .

SUE: Where / last / have it?

.... ?

PETE: I / not know. I / use / last night when I / buy / train ticket so I / must / have it then.

....

....

SUE: you / use it / since then?

.... ?

PETE: No. I suppose / might / lose it on / train or / I might / leave it / home this morning.

....

....

SUE: Why / you / phone home / check?

....

.... ?

b

STEVE: Where / you / be? / It / be / 11 o'clock!

.... !

ZENA: I / get / stuck / traffic.

....

STEVE: Well, you / should / phone!

.... !

ZENA: I / be / sorry, I / leave / mobile phone / home.

....

....

STEVE: But if I / know / you / be / late / I could / go / pub.

....

....

ZENA: I / be / really sorry.

....

Listen and read

Coincidences

7 **a)** 📼 Read and / or listen to these stories. Match the pictures opposite with each story. There are two pictures you do not need.

Ⓐ

I work in a market in London, just at the weekends – I've got a second-hand book stall, and one day I was getting my stall ready when an old lady came up and started looking at the books. She started chatting and telling me how she used to live in that part of London and how much it had changed
5 since she'd last been in the area. While we were talking, I put out a book and she picked it up. 'Oh, *Grimm's Fairy Tales*,' she said, 'I had a copy of this when I was a child. I used to read it again and again.' She began flicking through it and I carried on laying out the books, and when I looked up she was just standing there shaking, and she'd gone completely white. 'But ... but ... this
10 is my actual book,' she gasped, 'look, it's got my name, Joan, in it. How on earth did you get it?' Then she told me how there'd been a terrible fire while her family were away on holiday, and the house had been burnt to the ground. She thought all her belongings had been destroyed. She pulled out her purse to buy the book from me, but I stopped her. 'No, no ... please
15 accept it as a gift – it's such a wonderful story.'

Ⓑ

I was walking along the road in Windsor where I live, when I heard a phone ringing in a phone box, and something prompted me to go in and pick it up. There was a voice at the other end saying, in a very business-like way, 'Sorry to bother you at home, Julian, but I can't find that file you were working on. Do you
20 *remember where you put it?' It was Jasmine, who I work with at my office in London. I stopped her before she could go on. 'Jasmine, I'm in a phone box – how did you know I was here?' And she just said, 'Stop messing around, I'm really busy and I need that file.' I kept trying to convince her about where I was, but she just wouldn't believe me. Anyway, I told her where the file was, and then suddenly she*
25 *interrupted me: 'Julian! Hang on a minute I didn't dial your home phone number! I dialled the Windsor code, but then I dialled your security card number, which is next to your name in the book at work.' So somehow my security card number just happened to be the same number as the phone box that I was walking past.*

Ⓒ

A couple of years ago, we moved to an old house in the country. The man
30 *who lived there before had died, and we had to clear up a lot of his belongings. So we built a big bonfire at the end of the garden and took all the rubbish down there to burn. I'd just put a box full of stuff onto the fire, and I was standing chatting, when there was a bang, and I felt something hit the side of my head. I took my earring off and there was a bullet stuck in it, which had been*
35 *on the fire and had exploded. If I hadn't had the earrings on, it would've gone straight into my neck. And the scary thing was, the bullet had the letter 'J' on it – and my name's Jane – so it was as if this bullet was intended for me.*

b) Match each of the sentences below to one of the stories, A, B or C. There are four sentences for each story.

1 She must have felt astonished when she put the phone down. ....*B*....

2 The previous owner must have had a gun in the house. ....

3 He could have walked on without stopping. ....

4 She could have missed him if she'd come on a Friday. ....

5 She can't have been standing very far away from the fire. ....

6 She can't be living in the area now. ....

7 She must have been delighted with what she found. ....

8 'J' might have been the initial of the manufacturer's name. ....

9 The fire can't have destroyed everything. ....

10 She could have been killed. ....

11 Somehow he must have known the call was for him. ....

12 She can't have been concentrating. ....

c) Can you remember words from the texts to complete these phrases? Try doing them without looking and then check your answers.

1 The man was getting his stall *ready*............. when the old lady came up.

2 She started to flick .... a book.

3 He looked up and saw that she had .... completely white.

4 Jasmine thought Julian was messing .... at first.

5 She thought she had .... his home number.

6 The number .... to be the same number as the phone box.

7 The woman was clearing .... the dead man's belongings.

8 She put a box full of .... onto the bonfire.

9 She found a bullet .... in the earring.

Grammar snack

Need

8 **a)** Do the two sentences in 1–4 below mean the same or not?

1 Car Manual

Your new Victor 2.5 will **need a service** after the first 1000 kilometres, or six months, whichever is soonest.

the same

You will **need to service** your new Victor 2.5 after the first 1000 kilometres, six months, whichever is soonest.

2 Instructions

This medicine **needs keeping** out of the reach of children.

....

This medicine **needs to be kept** out of the reach of children.

3 An invitation

Tell Jim he **needn't wear** a tie – just a shirt and a jacket will be fine.

....

Tell Jim he **doesn't need to wear** a tie – just a shirt and a jacket will be fine.

4 A memo

The new secretary is great – I **needn't have written** out all the instructions for using Word 7.0, she's already an expert on it!

....

The new secretary is great – I **didn't need to write** out all the instructions for her, so it saved me a lot of time.

LOOK!

These sentences mean the **same**:

*I need **to wash** my hair*	*need* + infinitive
*My hair needs a **wash***	*need* + noun
*My hair needs **washing***	*need* + -ing form
*My hair needs **to be washed***	*need* + passive infinitive

*You don't need **to write** this down*	*not need* + infinitive
*You needn't **write** this down*	*needn't* + base form

These sentences have a **different** meaning:

*I **needn't have got up** early* (I got up early but it wasn't necessary)	*needn't* + *have* + Past Participle
*I **didn't need to get up** early* (It wasn't necessary and we don't know if I got up early or not)	*didn't need* + infinitive

---

b) Complete the gaps with a *need* construction, using a word from the box in the correct form. Some have more than one possibility.

> wait   take   worry   bring   cut improve   study   fix   glasses iron

1 You *needn't / don't need to worry* about me. I'll be OK.

2 I think I .... because I can't read this small print.

3 David's hair .... It's much too long!

4 Your writing's good but you .... your vocabulary.

5 You .... me to the airport. I'll get a taxi.

6 I .... so hard last night because we didn't have a test after all.

7 These trousers are great because they ....

8 Oh, you .... any wine, but thanks all the same.

9 We .... for long – the bus came almost immediately

10 My printer .... The paper keeps getting stuck.

Improve your writing

Formal and informal letters rearranging plans

9 **a)** Organise the following sentences into two letters, one formal and one informal. Write the two letters in your notebook using the letter extracts as your guide.

I will now be arriving on Friday 15th, staying until Tuesday 19th.

This obviously means that we'll have to put off going to see Claire and Annabelle until Saturday – I hope you can sort that out.

As you know, I had originally planned to arrive on Thursday 14th and stay until Monday 18th.

I would be grateful, therefore, if you would arrange for a car to collect me from Heathrow airport. My plane is due to land at 10.30 a.m.

It will also be necessary to postpone the scheduled meeting on Friday morning to late Friday afternoon and to inform all the people concerned.

Oh, and one last thing – will it be okay to stay until Tuesday morning? I'll assume it is, unless I hear from you.

This is just to let you know that something's come up at the office and I won't be able to get away until late on Friday.

I am writing with regard to my forthcoming visit in May.

I look forward to meeting you next month.

Hope you're well and looking forward to our weekend together.

If you have to go out just leave the key in the usual place.

Don't bother to come and pick me up, I'll just jump on a tube and make my own way to your place.

However, due to unforeseen circumstances, I am afraid that I will have to alter these arrangements.

Finally, would you mind contacting my hotel to change the room booking.

I've managed to get a ticket for a night train which gets into Waterloo early on Saturday morning.

If that is not possible, perhaps it could be arranged for Monday morning.

```
                        Magyar Porcelain Company,
                        1210 Budapest
                        Brasso ut. 122 I/7

                        17th March 19..

Ms. Hawley,
Secretary to the Board,
Magyar Porcelain Company,
3 Wessex Street,
London SW1 1MV

Dear Ms. Hawley,
I am writing with regard to my forthcoming visit in May.


Yours sincerely,

Zoltan Biro
```

Paris,
Monday afternoon

Dear Mark,

All the best,
Chantal

b) You have arranged to go on holiday with a friend (you decide where and when). You now want to bring another friend with you, and to go two days later. Write to your friend to change the arrangements.

module 10

Vocabulary
Organising an international event

1 a) Match a word or phrase from column A with one from column B to make a common expression.

	A		B
1	to be broadcast	a	an event
2	a lucrative	b	fee
3	a high	c	attention
4	to raise	d	to people
5	to appeal	e	someone's profile
6	to publicise	f	live
7	to attract	g	by someone
8	to compensate	h	contract
9	to be sponsored	i	someone for something

b) Complete the gaps in these sentences with one of the expressions above.

1 The concert will be _broadcast_ _live_ .... on NBC at 10 o'clock.

2 I think you should give the opening speech: it will .... your .... in the community.

3 We're going to .... the .... by putting up posters and handing out leaflets around town.

4 We're hoping that the games will .... of all ages.

5 This is the most .... advertising .... we've got this year – it should earn us $25,000.

6 Our plans for the opening night concert have already .... a lot of media ....

7 We're giving local people free tickets for the closing concert, to .... them .... the noise and extra traffic over the last few weeks.

8 Tonight's event is .... Bruhmann's Beer.

9 I don't think the speaker will ask for a very .... not more than £200, anyway.

Basic future forms
Will and *going to*

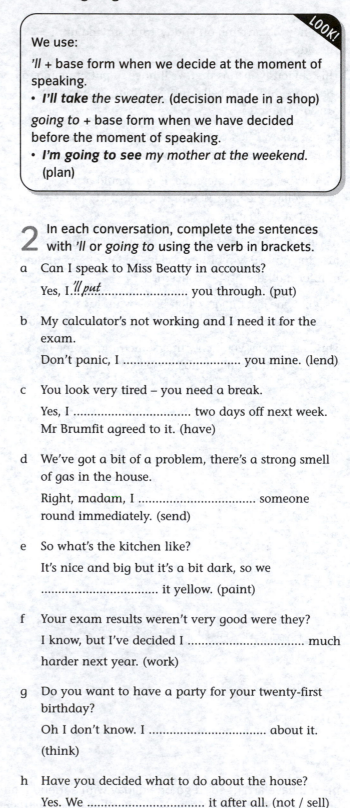

LOOK!

We use:

'll + base form when we decide at the moment of speaking.
- **I'll take** the sweater. (decision made in a shop)

going to + base form when we have decided before the moment of speaking.
- **I'm going to see** my mother at the weekend. (plan)

2 In each conversation, complete the sentences with *'ll* or *going to* using the verb in brackets.

a Can I speak to Miss Beatty in accounts?
Yes, I _'ll put_ .... you through. (put)

b My calculator's not working and I need it for the exam.
Don't panic, I .... you mine. (lend)

c You look very tired – you need a break.
Yes, I .... two days off next week. Mr Brumfit agreed to it. (have)

d We've got a bit of a problem, there's a strong smell of gas in the house.
Right, madam, I .... someone round immediately. (send)

e So what's the kitchen like?
It's nice and big but it's a bit dark, so we .... it yellow. (paint)

f Your exam results weren't very good were they?
I know, but I've decided I .... much harder next year. (work)

g Do you want to have a party for your twenty-first birthday?
Oh I don't know. I .... about it. (think)

h Have you decided what to do about the house?
Yes. We .... it after all. (not / sell)

Going to and Present Continuous for intentions and arrangements

3 In many situations you can use either the Present Continuous or *going to*. In the following sentences cross out the Present Continuous where it is **not** possible, because it is not something we can arrange.

a   Paula is going to become / ~~is becoming~~ a specialist in heart surgery when she finishes her training.

b   I'm going to have / I'm having a party on Saturday. Would you like to come?

c   I'm really going to enjoy / I'm really enjoying the concert tomorrow night.

d   My husband's going to see / seeing the doctor on Friday.

e   What time is your sister's plane going to leave / leaving?

f   Who are you going to meet / meeting for lunch today?

g   One day I'm going to meet / I'm meeting the girl of my dreams.

h   Peter keeps telling us he's going to make / he's making a million pounds before he's 40.

Phrases to express future ideas

4 In the following news items, rewrite the first sentence using the word in **bold** so that the meaning stays the same.

a   The Employment Secretary is going to spend more than £2 million on getting people back to work. **plans**

The Employment Secretary *plans to spend more than £2 million on getting people back to work* .

b   If all goes well, the Queen will visit several hospitals during her trip.   **hopes**

The Queen ....
....

c   The Minister is going to spend more time with his family.   **intends**

The minister ....
....

d   Management negotiators don't think they will reach an agreement before Friday.   **not expect**

Management negotiators ....
....

e   The President's meeting union representatives tomorrow.   **arranged**

The President ....
....

f   The Government is going to announce huge increases in petrol prices in the budget.   **due**

The Government ....
....

News Flash

Unemployment cut by 10%

g   The Government's goal is to cut unemployment by ten per cent this year.   **aims**

The Government ....
....

h   Florida is getting ready to receive thousands of people made homeless by yesterday's earthquake. **preparing**

Florida ....
....

Grammar snack

In case and if

LOOK!

We use **in case** to talk about what we do or did to be prepared for things which might happen.

• *Ruth took her camera **in case** she **wanted** to take some photos.*

Notice that when we talk about the future, we use the Present Simple.

• *Take a thick sweater **in case** it **gets** cold later.*

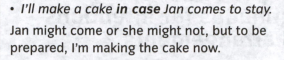

• *I'll make a cake **in case** Jan comes to stay.*

Jan might come or she might not, but to be prepared, I'm making the cake now.

• *I'll make a cake **if** Jan comes to stay.*

Jan might come or she might not, so I'll wait. If she comes, I'll make it.

5 **a)** Match the beginnings of the sentences in column A with the endings in column B, then put the verbs in the box in the correct form in the spaces.

| get (x2)   happen   forget   ~~not know~~   oversleep |

A

1 I've enclosed a map

2 I'd better write my cash card number down

3 I wrapped the present up very carefully

4 I'll give you a key

5 I had three alarm clocks next to the bed

6 It's always a good idea to take out holiday insurance

B

a in case you .... home before me.

b in case I ....

c in case something .... to your luggage.

d in case it .... broken in the post.

e in case I .... it.

f in case you *don't know* .... how to get to my house.

b) Complete these sentences with *if* or *in case*.

1 You'd better take an umbrella *in case* .... it rains.

2 We'll cancel the picnic .... it rains.

3 Ask at the school reception desk .... you lose anything.

4 Write your name in your dictionary .... you lose it.

5 Always cover yourself with insect repellant .... you get bitten by mosquitos.

6 You should see a doctor immediately .... you get bitten.

7 We'd better set the video to record *Bladerunner* .... we don't get back in time.

8 .... we get back in time, we can watch *Bladerunner* on TV.

Future Simple, Future Perfect or Future Continuous

6 **a)** Underline the best form of the verb in these sentences.

1 Do you think you *'ll still work* / *'ll still be working* / *'ll have worked* for Nabuko in five years' time?

2 Ten o'clock's fine: the meeting *will already start* / *will already be starting* / *will already have started*, but it doesn't matter if you come in late.

3 I'm afraid we can't use the school hall on Saturday afternoon. The decorators *won't finish* / *won't be finishing* / *won't have finished* by then.

4 Your uncle will be exhausted when he arrives because he *'ll drive* / *'ll be driving* / *'ll have driven* all the way from London.

5 Don't phone before two because we *'ll still have* / *'ll still be having* / *'ll still have had* lunch.

6 Don't worry, I'm sure Dr Jensen *will know* / *will be knowing* / *will have known* the answer.

7 I *'ll go* / *'ll be going* / *'ll have gone* past the supermarket on my way home from work anyway, so I can pick up some wine then.

b) Correct the mistakes with future forms in these dialogues.

1 (*2 mistakes*)

SECRETARY: When your plane gets in next Monday, a representative from our company, Mr Hashimoto, will be waiting for you.

MS JENKINS: How will I be recognising him? *recognise*

SECRETARY: He's quite tall and he'll have held a sign with your name on it. If you have any problems, just phone us immediately.

2 (*1 mistake*)

MRS GUNNER: I'm almost sick with worry.

TANIA: What time's Henry's operation?

MRS GUNNER: At 3.00 this afternoon.

TANIA: I'll be thinking of you both then. I'm sure it'll have been okay.

MRS GUNNER: I hope so.

3 (*1 mistake*)

ROB: I need to get this disk to Anne as soon as possible. Will you be seeing her today?

RIKKI: Yes, we've got a meeting with the sales department today at 3.30. I'll be giving it to her then.

ROB: Thanks.

4 (*2 mistakes*)

JACKIE: Will you be finishing your final exams by this time next week?

ELEANOR: Yes, by next Friday it'll all be over, thank goodness, and I'll have been my normal self again.

Pronunciation

Reading aloud: linking

When we speak, we link words in these ways:

- *I put on the light.*
  consonant → vowel

We pronounce **put on** as one word.

- *He arrived last week.*
  st → consonant
- *He left the next day.*
  xt → consonant

We don't pronounce the *t*.

- *Richard had a good day.*
  consonant → same consonant

We don't make separate sounds, we hold the sound a little longer.

7 **a)** 📼 Listen to the examples from the box on the cassette and repeat them.

b) Look at the dialogues 1 and 2 in exercise 6b and mark the links between the words and cross out any unnecessary *t* sounds.

e.g.

SECRETARY: When your plane gets in next Monday, a ...

c) 📼 Listen and repeat the dialogues, paying attention to the linking.

65

Reading

Fit for Life sports centre

Joyce and Simon have two children, Susie and Rachel. Joyce has decided to join the *Fit for Life* sports centre and has got a brochure which tells her about the prices, opening times, and types of exercise classes.

8 **a)** Write the correct prices in Joyce's notebook and check that your total is the same as hers.

Membership for me, Susie and Rachel

£ *130*

Swimming course for Susie

£ ....

Session in the Spa for me

£ ....

10 workout classes for Simon

£ ....

Induction and one visit to gym for me

£ ....

Squash court for Simon (half an hour)

£ ....

Total   £234.55

PRICES

| Annual Membership | Adult | £70 |
| | Child | £30 |

SWIM	Member	Non-member
Adult Swim	£2.10	£2.50
Junior Swim	£0.85	£1.20
Swim Course Adult	£35.00	£42.00
Swim Course Junior	£24.00	£29.30
Private Lessons (x6)	£80.00	£89.00

GYM	Member	Non-member
Induction	£15.00	£18.00
Per Visit	£5.50	£6.70

WORKOUT	Member	Non-member
Per Class	£4.00	£4.50
Tickets (x10)	£35.00	£41.00

See separate schedule for full programme of classes

SQUASH	Member	Non-member
45 mins	£6.30	£7.60
30 mins	£4.50	£5.30

THE SPA

Combining 2 Russian Steam Rooms, 3 Turkish Hot Rooms, Swedish Sauna, Ice Cold Plunge Pool, Jacuzzi, Relaxation Lounge and Public Swimming Pool.

	Member	Non-member
Per 3 hour session	£13.75	£18.40

Massage and beauty treatments available, see separate Spa leaflet for full details and prices.

Non-members admission / spectator

	Adult	Junior
	£0.75	£0.50

OPENING TIMES

SWIMMING

Monday – Friday	7am – 8pm
Saturday and Sunday	8am – 8pm
Monday – Friday	7am – 8am
	Earlybird Swim
Saturday	8am – 9am
	Earlybird Swim
Sunday	8am – 5pm
	Family Swim
Monday	3pm – 4pm
	Parent and under 4's
	(term time only)
Wednesday	8pm – 9pm
	Ladies only
Thursday	2pm – 3pm
	55+
Saturday	11am – 1.30pm
	Fun time
	1.30pm – 3pm
	Adult practice

Last admission is half an hour before closing
Children under the age of 8 must be accompanied in the water by an adult

GYM, SQUASH COURTS

Monday – Friday	7.30am – 10pm
Saturday and Sunday	8.00am – 8.30pm

For bookings call 0171 658 3214

THE SPA

Daily	10am – 10pm
Last entrance	8pm
Ladies' Day	Tuesday all day
Men's Day	Thursday all day

GENERAL INFORMATION

WORKOUT TIMETABLE		8–9	12–1	5–6	6–7	7–8
	Monday	Aerobics	–	Body Tone	Yoga	Aqua
	Tuesday	Step	Circuits	Body Max	Aqua	Step
	Wednesday	Aerobics	Step	Tai Chi	Body Tone	Circuits
	Thursday	Body Tone	Step	Yoga	Step	Circuits
	Friday	Aerobics	Body Max	Aqua	BodyTone	–
	Saturday	–	Tai Chi	–	Step	–
	Sunday	–	Aerobics			

WORKOUT CLASS ENTRY PROCEDURES

- Customers must sign in on arrival for booked classes five minutes prior to their commencement.
- After this time their class space will be resold.
- Customers will not be allowed to enter the studio after the commencement of the class.
- Please wear training shoes in all classes other than aqua and yoga.
- Customers must be aged sixteen and over to take part in our regular classes.

CLASS DESCRIPTIONS

Aerobics	A combination of moves and sequences which will improve your heart rate.
Aqua	A gentle workout in the swimming pool. The ability to swim is not required.
Body Tone	A class designed to tone and shape the muscles.
Body Max	Uses dumbbells in order to build up muscles.
Circuits	An intense workout for building up stamina. Recommended for sports specific training.
Step	Strengthen and tone your legs by stepping on and off a platform of varying heights.
Tai Chi	A Chinese martial art which uses slow graceful movement to co-ordinate mind and body.
Yoga	Breathing techniques, postures and relaxation to harmonise mind and body.

FIT FOR LIFE Sports Centre
Enquiries and bookings 0171 658 0022

b) Now answer these questions about the *Fit for Life* Sports Centre.

1 'Can I bring my two-year-old to the swimming pool when there are no older children around?' (Helen, 26)

   Yes, on Monday 3–4 p.m. .

2 'What's the latest time I can go into the pool on Saturday?' (Chris, 30)

   ....

3 'Is the swimming pool open at 8.00 p.m. on Wednesday?' (Dave, 30)

   ....

4 'Can I come for a swim on Thursday at 2.00 p.m.?' (Shan, 43)

   ....

5 'I'd like some gentle exercise to help relieve stress. Which classes do you suggest?' (Eva, 52)

   ....

6 'Can I wear any type of shoe in a Step class?' (Penny, 22)

   ....

7 'I'm recovering from a football injury and I'd like a class to help me regain my fitness. Which do you suggest?' (Stuart, 31)

   ....

8 'My Step class started ten minutes ago. Can I still go in?' (Lucy, 17)

   ....

9 'Can I do a Step class on Tuesday?' (Clare, 15)

   ....

10 'Is there a Circuits class between 5 and 7 in the evening?' (David, 31)

   ....

Improve your writing

Inviting a speaker

9 **a)** You are organising your language school's Social Club and you are writing to invite the English manager of your local football team to speak one evening. Here are the notes you made before writing.

suggested dates: Wed 10th, 17th, 24th
time: 7.30 p.m. (or later)
speak for about an hour, incl time for questions
fee?
join us for dinner afterwards?

You asked your teacher to look at the letter and she says there are fourteen grammatical mistakes in it! Find and correct the mistakes. The number of mistakes is given at the end of each line. The first one has been done for you.

Dear Mr Gough

I'm writing
I ~~write~~ on behalf of my school club for ask if you would be able to come and give   2

us talk about your work with the team. Many of our member are keen fans and   2

would love hear about the training and opportunities for amateur footballers. We   1

have Social Club events all Wednesday evenings and we are looking for speakers   2

for 10th, 17th or 24th March.

If you are able to come, I suggest the talk to start at 7.30 (later if you wish, of   1

course) and lasts about an hour, including time for people ask questions. Also,   1

we are delighted if you would join us for dinner after.   2

Please let us to know which date would suit you, and what would be your fee.   2

I do hope you will be able to come. I look forward to hear from you.   1

Yours sincerely,

....

b) Write a letter to invite a local English businessperson or celebrity to give a talk at your school. Start by writing notes, as in the example above.

Vocabulary

Sport and physical activities

10 a) Which of these sports is described in each of the paragraphs below?

sailing

cycling

swimming

aerobics

running

golf

1 'Once I got confident and learnt the basic strokes, there was no stopping me. Now I've persuaded my husband to take it up and he comes with me to the pool most times.' ....*swimming*....

2 'It really helped to strengthen my leg muscles and I've built up my stamina a lot. I love being in the open air but riding uphill is impossible!' ....

3 'I take it quite seriously and spend two hours training on the track every day. Once I've developed my skills and strength a bit more, I'd like to compete in a national race.' ....

4 'I just do it for fun, a couple of times a week. It's important to make sure you have a fully trained instructor who gives you enough time to warm up at the start. My body's definitely got much more flexible since I started.' ....

b) Complete the table below with words from the paragraphs above:

adjective	noun	verb
strong	*strength*	....
....	confidence	_____
....	flexibility	_____
competitive	competition / competitor	....
....	training	....

🔊 Listen to the cassette or say the words to yourself and mark the stress with a circle.

c) Match words in column A to words from column B from the paragraphs in exercise 10a to make common expressions.

A		B
1	build up	a training
2	do it	b a race
3	take it	c stamina
4	spend (two) hours	d seriously
5	take up	e for fun
6	compete in	f a hobby / a sport

d) Write a paragraph about a sport or physical activity that you enjoy doing or watching, explaining why you enjoy it. Use some of the words and phrases from exercises a, b and c.

module 11

Vocabulary
Medicine and science

1 **a)** Complete the chart with the noun form. Note that three are the same as the verb.

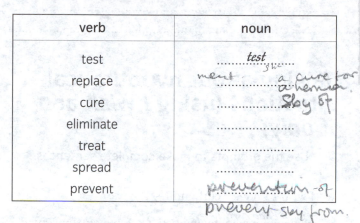

verb	noun
test	*test* ~~sth~~
replace	~~ment~~ a cure for a hernia
cure	Sky of
eliminate	....
treat	....
spread	....
prevent	~~prevention~~ of

prevent sky from.

b) Use these dictionary extracts from the *Longman Dictionary of Contemporary English* to check which prepositions are used with the nouns and verbs from the chart, then correct mistakes in five of the sentences opposite. The first has been done for you.

cure¹ /kjʊə‖kjʊr/ [v I] **1** to make someone who is ill well again: *When I left the hospital I was completely cured.* **2** to make an illness disappear completely, usually by medical treatment: *an operation to cure a hernia problem* **3** to remove a problem, or improve a bad situation: *Attempts to cure unemployment have so far failed.* | **cure sb of** *Even whisky could not cure him of his anxieties.*

cure² [n C] a medicine or medical treatment that can cure an illness: [+ **for**] *a cure for cancer* **2** something that removes a problem, or improves a bad situation: *a cure for inflation* **3** the act of making someone well again after an illness: *The new treatment effected a miraculous cure.*

pre·vent /prɪˈvent/ [v T] to stop something from happening, or stop someone from doing something: *The rules are intended to prevent accidents.* | **prevent sb / sth (from) doing sth** *Lacey has a back injury that may prevent him from playing in tomorrow's game.* – **preventable** adj

pre·ven·tion /prɪˈvenʃən/ [n N] the act of preventing something, or the actions that you take in order to prevent something happening: [+ **of**] *the prevention of war* | **crime / accident prevention** *Accident prevention is one of the main aims of the campaign.*

re·place /rɪˈpleɪs/ [v T] **1** to start doing something instead of another person, or being used instead of another thing: *I'm replacing Sue on the team.* **2** to remove someone from their job or something from its place, and put a different person or thing there: *Well, if he can't manage he'll have to be replaced.* | **replace sth with sth** *They're replacing the old windows with double glazing.*

spread /spred/ v past tense and past participle **spread** ► DISEASE / FEELING / PROBLEM / FIRE ◄ [I,T] to increase, or be increased, and affect more and more people or affect a larger area: *The fire spread very quickly.* | [+ **through / to / across** etc] *Cholera is spreading through the refugee camps at an alarming rate.* | **spread sth** *She's the sort of woman who enjoys spreading bad feeling.*

test [v]
► MEDICAL ◄ [T] to give someone a short medical examination on a part of their body, or to find out what is wrong with them: *I must have my eyes tested.* | **test sb for sth** *I'm going to test you for diabetes.*

treat·ment /ˈtriːtmənt/ [n]
► MEDICAL ◄ [C,U] a method that is intended to cure an injury or illness [+ **for**] *The best treatment for a cold is to rest and drink lots of fluids.* | **give sb treatment** *She was given emergency treatment by paramedics.* | **receive treatment** *receiving treatment for skin cancer* | **respond to treatment** (= get better when you are treated)

for

1   What's the most effective treatment ~~from~~ for a bad back?

2   We'll have to test the rest of the family ~~about~~ for hepatitis.

3   Johann never lets his disability prevent him ~~of~~ from enjoying life.

4   The virus is spreading through the whole school. They may have to close it and send the children home.

5   I'm going to have an operation on my knee. They're going to replace it with a metal one.

6   Scientists are still no nearer finding a cure ~~of~~ for AIDS.

7   Apparently, the best way to cure someone of a phobia is to make them confront it.

8   One of the Government's aims is the prevention ~~for~~ of alcohol consumption by under fourteen-year-olds.

c) Complete the sentences with a noun or verb from the chart, and with the correct preposition.

1   Hospitals are going to *replace*............... their old ambulances ....with........ more up-to-date ones.

2   Fortunately the firefighters were able to .....prevent... the fire .....from........ getting out of control.

3   In the last Olympic Games, many athletes were .....tested..........for........ drugs.

4   The fire .....spread.......many.. the whole building in under five minutes.

5   There is no known .....cure........for........... the common cold.

6   I don't think Emma'll ever be .....cured... of .... her fear of spiders.

Talking about hypothetical situations (using *if*, *supposing*, *imagine*)

2 **a)** Write the correct answer from the box below under each question and complete the gaps.

Patsy Clements

QUESTION TIME

The star of *Power Play*, NBC's new series about women in politics, answers our questions about her dreams and ambitions.

1 *Would* .... you be a good politician?
(f) No, I don't think I would ....

2 What one thing would you change about yourself if you ....?
....

3 Supposing you weren't in your present job, what would you be doing now?
....

4 Imagine you .... world leader, what would your first act be?
....

5 If you .... live in a TV series, what would it be?
....

6 Supposing you .... reborn, what .... you come back as?
....

7 In a natural disaster, which one possession would you rescue from your home?
....

8 If you .... change one thing you've done in your life, what would it be?
....

a I'm happy with the way I am.
b My lap top computer: I .... live without it.
c I .... be a stand up comedian, or I .... be a night club singer.
d A cat. I love lying in the sun, and doing nothing!
e The time I agreed to do a ketchup advert, dressed as a tomato.
f No, I don't think I *would* ....
g I'd resign straightaway!
h Star Trek. I'd like to travel round the universe.

b) Answer the same questions about yourself.

1 ....
2 ....
3 ....
4 ....
5 ....
6 ....
7 ....
8 ....

Talking about hypothetical situations (using *I wish* and *if only*)

3 Use the prompts to make complete sentences.

a I wish / I have / curly hair.
I wish I had curly hair ....

b If only I / can / drive.
....

c I wish Sally / speak up. I can hardly hear her.
....

d I wish I / be / at home now.
....

e If only I / not get / so nervous before exams.
....

f I wish you / shut up / and / listen / to me.
....

It's time

4 Rewrite these sentences so that they mean the same, using *it's time*.

a Susan ought to get a job.
It's time Susan got a job ....

b We'd better go home now.
....

c The children should be in bed now.
....

d Jo should realise that money doesn't grow on trees.
....

e Why don't you learn to cook for yourself!
.... !

f I must buy myself a new watch.
....

Talking about hypothetical situations in the past (using *if*)

5 In these hypothetical situations, complete the two possible endings (one about the present and one about the past) with the correct form of the verb in brackets.

1 If Julie and Sam hadn't had that terrible row,

a) they *wouldn't have split up* .

b) they ....
together now.

(not split up / still be)

2 If the banks had been more honest,

a) we ....
in such a mess.

b) the stock market ....

(not be / not collapse)

3 If Ed had given up smoking ten years ago,

a) I'm sure he ....
fitter.

b) he ....
a fortune.

(be / save)

4 If I hadn't lent Emma the car,

a) I ....
you a lift to the station.

b) she ....
to go to Cambridge.

(give / not be able)

5 If Tammi had made a back-up copy of her files,

a) she ....
them all.

b) she ....
them now.

(not lose / not retype)

Talking about hypothetical situations in the past (using *I wish* and *if only*)

6 Complete the sentence under each picture using a verb from the box below.

| eat | buy | wear | bring | come | study |

1 I wish *I hadn't worn these shoes* .

2 I wish ....
.... my umbrella .

3 I wish ....
.... to this party .

4 If only ....
.... all those chocolates .

5 I wish ....
.... this dress .

6 If only ....
.... harder .

71

Talking about hypothetical situations in the present and past (using *I wish* and *if only*)

> **LOOK!**
>
> In conversation we often just use an auxiliary instead of repeating the verb:
>
> - *Can you play the piano?*
>   *No, but I wish I could play the piano.*
>
> - *Did you watch* First Sight *on television last night?*
>   *No, but I wish I had watched it. Everybody said it was great.*

7 Put the correct auxiliary verb in the spaces in the sentences. (e.g. *did, didn't, would, wouldn't, had, hadn't, could, couldn't*)

a It's a pity you didn't come to the party.

   Yes I wish I *had* . I didn't get anything done at home.

b Has Jim applied for the director's job?

   Yes, but now he wishes he ...hadn't... . He doesn't really want all that extra responsibility.

c I'm thinking of doing a computer course.

   I wish you would . It might mean you could leave that awful job of yours.

d Did you bring any water?

   No, I wish I ...had... . I didn't realise it would be so hot.

e Will Sally be able to come to dinner?

   No, she wishes she ...could... but she's got to revise for her exams.

f You're under thirty aren't you?

   I wish I ...was... ! No, I'm thirty-five.

g Are you going to the school play tonight?

   Yes, but I wish I ...wasn't... . I'm absolutely exhausted and I just want to collapse in front of the TV.

Reading

The science of chronobiology

Read the text on the next page and answer the following questions.

8 **a)** Are the following statements true (*T*) or false (*F*)?

1 Chronobiology is the study of clock making. ......*F*......

2 Chronobiology could help you to make the best use of your time. ......*T*......

3 We don't need watches because we have an internal body clock. ......*F*......

4 If you stay out late regularly, it won't upset your body clock, provided that you stay in bed the next morning. ......*F*......

5 Shift workers are more likely to get ill than people who have regular work times. ......*T*......

6 It is easy to lose concentration in the early hours of the morning. ......*T*......

7 It would be a good idea for international athletes to travel to an event two weeks before it starts. ......*T*......

b) When is a **good** time to do the following activities? Look at the texts in the diagram and cross out any activities which are in the **wrong** time period.

6 a.m. – 8 a.m.	clean your teeth avoid people with colds ✓ have a shower do a workout *afterwn*
8 a.m. – 1 p.m.	study try a new restaurant *see 5~7* drink alcohol
1 p.m. – 5 p.m.	have a sleep have a shower do a workout ✓ play tennis ✓
5 p.m. – 8 p.m.	try a new restaurant ✗ play tennis have a sleep
8 p.m. – midnight	study go to bed drink alcohol ✓ eat
midnight – 6 a.m.	sleep clean your teeth do a workout

Take time out to visit the crazy world of Chronobiology – an increasingly popular science that goes something like this: you and every other animal on the planet has a 'body clock' that controls rhythms on a day / night cycle (a sort of internal physiological timekeeper). This clock is governed by hormones that determine the best times for us to perform physiological and psychological tasks – whether it's to do with building new muscle tissue or recovering from last night's party.

The hormone that makes you feel sleepy is melatonin, whereas other hormones, such as cortisol, kickstart your body in the morning. In several experiments, volunteers who have been cut off from sunlight, newspapers, TV and all other contact with the outside world, have shown that human body clocks are 'naturally' set to a 25-hour cycle. Watches and clocks are needed to keep our bodies attuned to a 24-hour routine. The day / night cycle is a definite help. The blind, who are deprived of this natural time-keeper, have to keep to a strict routine – taking meals at regular times, for example, and going to bed at the same time every day – in order to avoid falling into the 25-hour cycle.

Small changes to our internal clock, such as missing a night's sleep, are tolerated by the body. But constant major disturbances, like regular periods of wild partying followed by getting up late, can badly upset your timekeeping. Sleep expert Jim Horne, from Loughborough University, recommends getting up at the same time every day – whether you're working or not. This, he says, readjusts your body clock so that you feel sleepy at roughly the same time every night.

Shift workers, for instance, nearly always suffer from their working patterns – not because they have to work anti-social hours (given a few days, the body can adapt to this reasonably well), but because their shift times continually change: the body never settles into a set pattern, leading to confusion, fatigue and a lowered immunity to disease.

This can be especially dangerous in professions where constant high concentration is vital. We are at our lowest ebb between 2 am and 4 am, when body temperature is at its lowest and statistics show that this is when most industrial accidents and errors occur. The Chernobyl disaster in Russia and the Union Carbide poison gas leaks at Bhopal in India both occurred in the early hours because workers were feeling sleepy.

Studies have shown that flying across time zones makes the body incapable of distinguishing between day and night. Travellers are nearly always tired or hungry at the 'wrong times'. Their body clock eventually adjusts, but it can take up to two weeks. Athletes competing in international events must plan their travelling arrangements carefully so that they're in prime condition.

1am	2am	3am	4am	5am	6am	7am	8am	9am	10am	11am	12am	1pm	2pm	3pm	4pm	5pm	6pm	7pm	8pm	9pm	10pm	11pm

How your efficiency varies over 24 hours ...

Don't catch a cold
Avoid your neighbour's sick child first thing in the morning – your immune system is weakest between 6am and 8am when the quantity of white blood cells is at its lowest.

Best time to learn
In the morning, your short term memory is at its best. But you'll have to relearn all that info after lunch if you want to remember it in a week's time. Work that one out.

Do your body building
Bodybuilders should aim to schedule their iron pumping sessions for the afternoons – you'll hardly gain anything from a morning session, regardless of how much pain you endure. And forget working out under the midnight oil – late-night exercise will keep you awake.

Poor taste
Don't make a late booking for that new haute cuisine restaurant: your sense of taste and smell is at its peak between 5pm and 7pm.

Drink up, but hold the grub
Put an end to those late-night snacks – the stomach doesn't work well at night. The liver, on the other hand speeds up after 8pm, which is why you can drink more alcohol in the evening than earlier in the day.

The Zzzzzzz factor
We become tired between 1pm and 2pm because our inner clock is telling us we need a siesta. Other natural 'mini-breaks' occur at 9am and around 5pm. No wonder you always nod off on the train.

Brush your teeth now
During the day, the glands inside your mouth produce an alkaline solution that kills bacteria and helps protect your teeth against decay. But they don't work from midnight to 6am.

When to wash'n'go
Showers and saunas are most invigorating in the afternoon: this is when your blood vessels are more likely to dilate, so allowing optimum circulation and toxin elimination.

Time your tennis challenge
Reaction speeds are fastest in the early evening. But they're at their slowest just after 3pm – so careful who you challenge to tennis.

Time to sleep
It's not called 'beauty sleep' for nothing, you know: going to bed before midnight allows skin cells to regenerate themselves from 11pm to 1am (providing we're asleep). While hair and nail growth is fastest between 4pm and 6pm.

Improve your writing
Reporting opinions

The director of your school has recently been given a sum of money to spend on improvements. She has suggested using it to transform an empty room at the back of the school into either a quiet study room or a coffee bar. She has organised a competition for people to write articles for the school notice board, saying which option students would prefer.

9 a) Look at articles A and B below. Which one do you think won the competition?

A

boring

The results of the survey on whether to have a quiet study room or a coffee bar.

I asked over thirty students whether they thought the money recently given to the school should be spent on a coffee bar or a quiet study room and most people said they'd like a coffee bar. There were lots of reasons for this. Some people don't like studying on their own. Other people think it's better to talk to people in English. A coffee bar would be a good place to relax and talk to people in English. A few people wanted somewhere quiet to do their homework but most people want somewhere where they can meet people from other classes. The result is that students are in favour of a coffee bar.

?

B

The loneliness of the quiet room studier

Do you really learn English by studying on your own? Most people would say you make more progress by speaking English than by burying your head in a book.

I asked over 30 students about the coffee bar versus quiet room issue, and apart from two who couldn't make up their minds, the overwhelming majority opted, sensibly, for a coffee bar. Why? Well, some find studying alone boring, others think the relaxed atmosphere of a coffee bar would help them to activate their English, especially if it was declared an 'English-only zone'. One imaginative person also suggested that lesson fees could be reduced for anyone who worked behind the bar.

Whilst a few people would appreciate, after a busy day at work, somewhere quiet to do their homework before lessons, most would prefer a more sociable environment where they could get to know people from other classes.

All in all then, it seems: although 'silence is golden', coffee, cake and English chit-chat win the day. */ conclusion*

b) Article B won because it is written in a much better style.

1 Why is its title better?
It is shorter and it has an interesting title.

2 Find two examples of rhetorical questions (questions which do not expect an answer, but which are used to involve the reader).
Do you really
Why?

3 Article A has only one paragraph while Article B has four. What is the purpose of each?
Paragraph 1 *Introduction*
Paragraph 2 *survey report. +*
Paragraph 3 *survey nep*
Paragraph 4 *Conclusion*

4 How many times is *people* used in Article A?
8

Find six ways that Article B avoids repeating *people*.
they   students   majority
some   others   most.

5 The sentences in Article B are much longer than those in Article A. In Article B what is the purpose of these linking words or phrases?

| to add an idea   to make a contrast (x3) |
| to show an exception   to summarise |
| to give emphasis |

Paragraph 2   apart from .... *exception*
                some ... others .... *contrast*
                especially if .... *emphasis*
                also *to add an idea*

Paragraph 3   Whilst a few people ... most
                .... *contrast*

Paragraph 4   All in all .... *summarize*
                although .... *contrast*

c) The director of your school has proposed that the school should be non-smoking and has invited students to write articles giving their opinions. Write an article giving your classmates' opinions on this issue.

Vocabulary

Prefixes and suffixes

1 **a)** Form negatives from the adjectives in the box which can all be used to describe the media, and complete the chart below.

biased	predictable	responsible	reliable
suitable	harmful	accurate	informative
convincing	sensitive	thoughtful	aware
appealing	relevant	offensive	tolerant

un-	in-	ir-	-less
unbiased			

b) Complete the gaps with one of the adjectives above, in the positive or negative.

1 The documentary got a lot of facts wrong.

Yes, it was really ....*inaccurate*............... .

2 I'm getting bored with that soap opera. You always know what's going to happen next.

Yes, it's getting really ....

3 That series has got rather a lot of strong language. Do you let Naomi watch it?

No, I think it's .... for young children.

4 Why did they talk about what the Minister was wearing? It had nothing to do with her speech.

Yes, it was completely .... , wasn't it?

5 The paparazzi never think about people's feelings.

Yes, they're so ....

6 I know that game show's a bit stupid, but at least it doesn't hurt anyone.

Yes, I suppose it's quite ....

7 The programme was quite unbalanced, I thought. They gave much more air time to the Democrats.

I agree, I thought it was really .... too.

Pronunciation

Word stress

2 **a)** 🔲 Listen to the adjectives in the box or say them aloud to yourself and show the stress patterns with circles.

biased	predictable	responsible	reliable
suitable	harmful	accurate	informative
convincing	sensitive	thoughtful	aware
appealing	relevant	offensive	tolerant

b) 🔲 Listen to the jazz chant and say it with the cassette, or read it aloud to yourself.

The boy next door?

I'm marrying the boy next door
He's organised and sensible
My mother thinks he's marvellous
The boy from number four.

'He's really just so suitable
Reliable, responsible
A thoughtful boy, predictable
What could you ask for more?'

My mother's view's irrelevant
She seems to be quite unaware
I find him unappealing
Her future son-in-law.

I want him unpredictable
Unsuitable, intolerant
A little unreliable
My fantasy amour.

The letter that I'm leaving them's
Convincing and informative
It tells them that I've gone in search
Of someone to adore.

Listen and read

Attitudes towards television

3 **a)** 📼 Read and / or listen to these people talking about the role of television in their lives and then answer the questions below.

1 Who exists quite happily without TV?   *Veronica*..........

2 Who sees TV as a central part of their life?

....

3 Who has recently been disappointed by TV programmes?   ....

4 Who uses TV to give a sense of structure to their life?

....

5 Who wants everyone to try doing without TV?

....

6 Who has a TV but doesn't let it rule their life?

....

Ⓐ Emily

I'm afraid to say my life revolves around TV. As soon as I get up every
5 *morning I look at the TV guide to see what I want to video, and make sure I set the video before I leave for work. I then often plan my evenings around things*
10 *I've videoed and things which are on TV that night. Personal favourites are 'Newsnight', any detective series and any fly-on-the-wall documentary. I love seeing people's true colours exposed when they're*
15 *under the eye of the camera. Some Sundays I find that I have so many videos to watch that I have to devote a whole day to catching up on them. Don't get me wrong, I do have a social life of sorts and I*
20 *don't get withdrawal symptoms if I miss an episode of one of my favourite soaps, but I like the ritual that planning my TV viewing gives me.*

Ⓑ Veronica

Our TV is sitting
25 *in the attic collecting dust. We decided it was taking up too much space in our living room*
30 *and in our lives so we banned it completely. Our children were quite young at the time and we didn't want them to turn into couch potatoes. Their lives now, I believe, are much richer and fuller – they spend a lot of the*
35 *time playing together and making things and they've each taken up a musical instrument. I know some people think we're odd, but I think the evidence shows that my children are not bored or missing out on anything. I'm only now*
40 *beginning to realise how much time we used to waste in front of the box – in fact I'm not quite sure how we'd fit TV into our lives now! I'd like to think that if people switched off their television even just for one week, they'd discover how much*
45 *more to life there is than The Oprah Winfrey Show or Cheers.*

Ⓒ Guy

I think I'm quite selective in my viewing habits. The TV doesn't dominate my life and given the choice I could take it or leave
50 *it. I'd never come home and switch it on just for want of anything better to do. Documentaries in particular have always fascinated me, probably because I always feel they are very informative. That is until recently when I read a worrying article about*
55 *how a lot of them are fixed in some way. For instance, there was one documentary which featured an interview with a millionaire drug dealer who turned out to be an unemployed accountant, and another one, a consumer watchdog programme in which a cockroach was planted in the kitchen of a restaurant in order to make the report more*
60 *dramatic. This kind of thing has brought home to me the fact that TV is just another commercial enterprise vying for an audience, and you can't always believe what you see on the screen.*

b) Find a word or phrase in the texts which means:

1 forbidden   *banned (line 30)*.

2 someone who watches TV a lot
....

3 strange   ....

4 is centred around
....

5 a set of TV programmes that have the same characters in a different story each week
....

6 a programme which shows people's daily lives in a natural way
....

7 the painful feelings you experience when you stop a habit such as smoking, drinking alcohol, etc
....

8 a programme which investigates businesses / shops to protect the rights of customers
....

9 a large insect which lives in dirty places, e.g. kitchens
....

10 competing for   ....

c) Read the texts again and answer these questions.

1 Are Veronica's children allowed to watch TV if they want to?

2 According to Veronica, what are two advantages of not having a TV?

3 How does Emily find time to watch all her videos?

4 Does Emily ever go out with friends?

5 In Guy's story, where does the cockroach in the kitchen come from?

6 Why were the documentaries fixed in the ways Guy describes?

Vocabulary
The media

4 Cross out the word which does not belong to each category. Use a dictionary like the *Longman Dictionary of Contemporary English* to help you if necessary.

1 **People who work behind the scenes for TV**
costume designer, make-up artist, viewer, continuity person, floor manager

2 **People who appear on TV**
chat show host, cartoonist, presenter, news reader, commentator

3 **Sections of a newspaper**
editorial, obituaries, domestic news, headlines, listings

4 **Types of TV programme**
a series, a consumer watchdog programme, a novel, a fly-on-the-wall documentary, a current affairs programme

5 **Things you can do with a TV remote control**
turn the TV up, change the channel, channel hop, take the TV off, adjust the colour

6 **Adjectives to describe magazines**
glossy, down-market, teen, live, specialist

Reporting people's exact words

5 a) Put the sentences in the correct order and write them in the correct category below. The first word is underlined.

1 put – if – asked – I'd – on – <u>He</u> – me – weight
2 me – was – reduce – boss – <u>My</u> – going – he – salary – told – to – my
3 the – in – exam – <u>She</u> – I'd – said – cheated
4 kiss – I'd – me – <u>Jimmy</u> – if – give – asked – a – him
5 beautiful – <u>Michael</u> – had – thought – I – said – eyes – he
6 <u>Andi</u> – had – teacher – ever – was – best – added – he'd – I – the – that

A time when someone said something …

A   … rude or cheeky
   1 He asked me if I'd put on weight ....
   ....

B   … flattering or complimentary
   ....
   ....

C   … ridiculous or unfair
   ....
   ....

b) Complete the dialogues, using information from the speech bubbles.

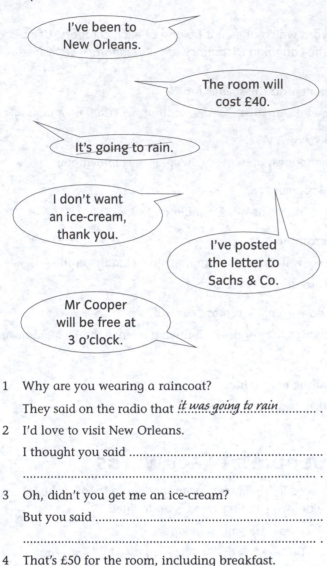

I've been to New Orleans.

The room will cost £40.

It's going to rain.

I don't want an ice-cream, thank you.

I've posted the letter to Sachs & Co.

Mr Cooper will be free at 3 o'clock.

1 Why are you wearing a raincoat?
  They said on the radio that *it was going to rain* .

2 I'd love to visit New Orleans.
  I thought you said ....
  ....

3 Oh, didn't you get me an ice-cream?
  But you said ....
  ....

4 That's £50 for the room, including breakfast.
  But I was told ....
  ....

5 I'm afraid Mr Cooper's in a meeting.
  But when I spoke to you earlier, you said ....
  ....

6 I can't find the letter to Sachs & Co. anywhere.
  But you told me just now that ....
  ....

Verbs that summarise what people say

6 **a)** Only four of these sentences are correct. Correct the others, using verbs from the box. The first one has been done for you.

> threaten   agree   deny   refuse   blame   complain
> warn   persuade   promise   assure   decide

promised
1 Simon ~~threatened~~ to bring Josie some expensive perfume from Paris.

2 The President refused having an affair with his secretary.

3 We're trying to persuade our boss to give us an extra day's holiday in the summer.

4 Tony accused the late nights at his office for the breakup of his marriage.

5 Paula wanted to drive home from the party, but we decided her to take a taxi.

6 Sonia suggested booking a table in case the restaurant got very busy.

7 The car dealer urged me that his prices were the lowest in town.

8 I'm sure we'd all like to congratulate Andre on winning the championship.

9 The company offered to double Jeremy's salary if he would stay on.

10 At the end of the evening, we concluded to meet the next day.

b) Rewrite the sentences using a summarising verb from exercise 6a, so that the meaning stays the same.

1 Let's hire a van and travel round Europe.

He _suggested hiring a van and travelling around Europe_ .

2 No, I'm not going to pay.

She ....

....

3 I didn't break the photocopier, honestly.

She ....

....

4 This food is undercooked.

She ....

....

5 Be careful Pat, the roads are very slippery.

She ....

....

6 If you don't turn that noise down, I'm going to call the police.

She ....

....

7 Would you like me to have a look at your TV?

He ....

....

8 The misunderstanding was your fault, Geoff.

She ....

....

Grammar snack
Passive reporting verbs

LOOK!

Active

• _People say that she is a millionaire._
she is living in Argentina.
she has left her husband.

Passive

• **It is said that** _she is a millionaire._
she is living in Argentina.
she has left her husband.

• **She is said to be** _a millionaire._
to be living _in Argentina._
to have _left her husband._

• The two passive forms are often used in news reports.

• Other verbs that follow this pattern are:

believed, thought, reported, expected, understood, known considered, estimated, claimed

7 Rewrite these sentences so that they mean the same, using passive structures.

a Reports coming in estimate that 500 people have died in the earthquake.
500 people are estimated to have died in the earthquake .

b The police believe that the terrorists are hiding somewhere south of the city.
The terrorists ....

c Our correspondent thinks that the rebel troops are only a few kilometres from the city.
The rebel troops ....

d We understand that the two Prime Ministers are close to reaching an agreement.
It ....

e We expect that the air traffic controllers' strike will end in the next few hours.
The air traffic controllers' strike ....

f Many people consider _Citizen Kane_ to be the best film ever made.
Citizen Kane ....

g Scientists claim that this new drug increases your life expectancy.
It ....

h People say that Mick Riek and Mel Court are honeymooning in the Bahamas.
Mick Riek and Mel Court ....

i Local sources reported that thousands of people were homeless after the flood.
Thousands of people ....

79

Improve your writing

Correcting written information

8 a) Cecilia went on a day trip to Bath and Stonehenge in England. Look at the notes she made on the advertisement, then complete her letter to the company with a word or phrase from the box.

DAY TRIP TO
Bath and Stonehenge

arrived 40 minutes late **Sunday August 16th** only tours booked in advance – we hadn't booked!

10.00 We arrive in the historic city of Bath and tour the Roman Baths

11.30 Free time: taste the water from the underground springs and stroll through the old streets full of souvenir shops

or *too crowded, many shops closed*

visit the Museum of Costume —— *closed!*
and admire the architecture of the Circus and Crescents —— *not enough time to do this*

1.00 We go on to Stonehenge

touch the old stones – site of Druid sacrifices —— *can't touch the stones – all behind big wire fences*

relax in the peace and quiet of the English countryside

5.00 We return to London

BARGAIN TOURS LTD, UK.

Dear Sir

I am writing (1) <u>with regard to</u>.............. the day trip to Bath on Sunday August 16th, organised by your company. I and my friends were disappointed with the trip for several reasons.

(2) .... , we arrived in Bath forty minutes late and (3) .... had less time there than we had been told.

(4).. , the advert promised that we would tour the Roman Baths, but we found that a tour had not been booked for us.

(5) .... , several places were closed, including some shops and the Museum of Costume.

(6).. , the advert suggested visiting the Circus and the Crescents, but we didn't have enough time.

(7) .... the visit to Stonehenge, this was a further disappointment. Your advert claimed that we could touch the stones, (8) .... they are actually behind big wire fences.

(9) .... , we feel that the trip was not worth the £30 that we each paid, and we would appreciate some form of compensation for our disappointment.

I look forward to hearing from you,

Yours faithfully,

Cecilia Johnson

therefore	all in all	<u>with regard to</u> to begin with
secondly	in addition	whereas as for
on top of all this		

b) Imagine that you took some English visitors on a sightseeing trip to a place of interest in your country, but were disappointed. Write a letter to the UK tour organisers pointing out how the trip was different from their advertisement.

Think about these questions before you write:

- Were the times the same as in the advertisement?
- Were all the places open?
- Did you have to pay any extra money?
- Did you have enough time to see places?
- Were the descriptions of the places accurate?

Answer key

module 1

Vocabulary
Phrasal verbs to talk about your life map

1 **a)**

Happiest: his childhood
Saddest: when he first moved to Johannesburg

c)
2   to get through   5   to get by
3   to bring up   6   to take up
4   to settle down

d)
2   I don't know how I got through the year.
3   My husband's taken up jogging because he was so unfit.
4   It wasn't until he was forty-five that my brother settled down.
5   How will they get by?
6   I was brought up by my grandparents.

Reading
2 **b)**

2   Robert   6   Celine
3   Robert   7   Robert
4   Rodrigo   8   Robert / Claire
5   Claire

c)
2   have (to have a go at doing something)
3   lost (to lose control of something)
4   for (to go for a walk)
5   have (to have little / a lot / not much in common)
6   the (to get / have the shock of your life)

Grammar check-up
Verb forms

3 **a)**

1   d   5   c
2   e   6   g
3   f   7   a
4   h   8   b

Present Perfect or Past Simple
4

2   b   5   b
3   b   6   b
4   a

Present Perfect or Past Perfect
5

b   had   f   's / has
c   've / have   g   'd / had
d   's / has, hasn't   h   's / has
e   'd / had

Past Simple, Present Perfect or Past Perfect
6

Text A
2   happened   4   had lost
3   started   5   gave

Text B
1   has never had   4   managed
2   didn't have   5   has written
3   has become

Future forms
7

b   Just a moment, I'll **look** in my bag.
e   Yes, I'll **take** it.
f   My niece Emma **is going to be** a doctor when she grows up.

Auxiliary verbs
Adding emphasis

8

2   d   Ben **does** look well. Has he been on holiday?
3   a   I **do** hate it when people are late for meetings.
4   c   We didn't like the hotel, but we **did** enjoy the tours.
5   f   She **did** tell us she was going away. Don't you remember?
6   b   I **do** like fish generally, but I don't like it raw.

Sounding interested
9

b   Has she?   How long has she had it?
c   Hasn't he?   I hope he enjoys it.
d   Aren't you?   Why not?
e   Do you?   I don't.
f   Wasn't there?   It's okay, I've got some chicken.

Tag questions
10

b   You aren't married, are you?
    or   You're not married, are you?
c   Miss Peters left Brazil on Saturday, didn't she?
d   The 1980 Olympics were held in Seoul, weren't they?
e   I'm meeting / I am meeting Bill Townsend this afternoon, aren't I?
f   There wasn't much food at the party, was there?

Avoiding repetition
11

b   Well, John has, but Trevor and Ann haven't.
c   Yes, I am actually.
d   Yes it does, for two hours.
e   I think it has, but I'll check for you.
f   No it wasn't, but it was very cold.
g   No, I won't.

Pronunciation
Weak forms

12 a)

2 I've heard a lot about you.
3 Where are you from originally?
4 Do you have any family?
5 Do you live locally?
6 What do you do for a living?
7 What exactly does your job involve?
8 How long have you worked there?
9 Do you know many other people here?
10 Is this your first visit to London?

Improve your writing
Linking phrases for a personal profile

13 a)

2	d	5	g	8	e
3	c	6	h	9	b
4	i	7	a	10	f

module 2

Vocabulary
Word building with abstract nouns, verbs and adjectives

1

Text A
2 anxious
3 disturbing
4 personal
5 pressure(s)
6 envy

7 dramatic
8 relationships
9 scientists
10 memory

Text B
1 violence
2 research
3 exciting
4 involved
5 suffering

6 fantasies
7 worrying
8 imaginary
9 reality
10 tragic

Pronunciation
Nouns and verbs

2 a)

noun	verb	noun	verb
decrease	decrease	record	record
support	support	insult	insult
control	control	damage	damage
increase	increase	transport	transport
promise	promise	surprise	surprise
import	import	export	export

b) 🔲

1 Which football team do you support?
2 Myra damaged her car badly in the accident.
3 I work for an import–export company.
4 Unfortunately, there's been a huge increase in burglaries recently.
5 Do you keep a record of all your expenses?
6 Sam lost control of the motorbike on an icy road.
7 The shop promised to have my shoes ready by today.

Improve your writing
Spelling

3 a) *-ible / -able* adjectives

flexible   advisable   noticeable   incredible
believable   washable

b) *-ent / -ant* adjectives
independent   urgent   efficient
innocent   unpleasant   arrogant
inconvenient   inconsistent   incompetent
obedient   confident

c) *-er / -or*

-er	*-or*
interpreter	inventor
trainer	supervisor
interviewer	translator
teacher	operator
manager	director
reporter	actor

Listen and read
What makes you anxious?

4 b)

1 Being late for something.
2 Worse.

c)
2 a – 'the problem refused to disappear until an hour or so after the train or plane – or whatever it was – had been safely caught.'   (lines 7–9)
3 a – 'she used to move about from room to room until her husband … finally joined her … .'   (lines 14–16)
4 c – 'It is not, of course, certain that this is what he did' … it was hard to believe that he was not purposely causing pain to the unhappy lady. … had wanted to miss the train, simply to increase the poor woman's suffering.'
(lines 20–21, 23–24, 30–31)
5 b – 'there had been times recently when she had begun to wonder.'   (lines 38–39)

Abstract and general ideas
Gerunds (*-ing* forms)

5 a)

eating sensibly.
not drinking alcohol at lunch.
not taking work home.
getting at least 7 hours' sleep each night.
not talking about business at home.
drinking mineral water instead of strong coffee.
taking a daily 'power nap'.
not going to bed after 11 o'clock during the week.
not eating fattening snacks between meals.

b)

b   Making new friends is easy.

c   I hate not remembering / not being able to remember people's names.

d   Having worked for twelve hours in the office, Jack decided to go home.

e   My mother-in-law can't stand people smoking when she's eating.

f   I find that having a nice long bath is a good way to relax.

6 a)

2	F	5	T
3	T	6	F
4	F	7	F

b)

2   I'm getting used to Sally's Irish accent.

3   Linda isn't used to eating very late at night.

4   I can't get used to people bowing when they meet.

5   I'll never get used to the weather here.

c)

2   Because they're used to eating with chopsticks. / Because they're not used to eating with a knife and fork.

3   Yes, until you get used to them. / Yes, until you get used to wearing them.

4   Because they aren't used to the sun. / Because they aren't used to sunbathing.

5   It can be, until you get used to it. / It can be, until you get used to riding one/it.

Prefixes

7 a)

I	M	P	A	T	I	E	N	T	S	R	K
L	U	X	T	C	T	U	N	E	V	E	N
L	O	W	F	A	T	C	E	Q	P	P	Z
E	C	E	E	A	M	I	S	R	E	A	D
G	K	L	O	M	B	E	V	E	P	Y	S
I	S	L	I	I	X	N	A	P	U	T	E
B	A	K	R	S	I	O	W	L	S	A	Y
L	O	N	Y	S	W	N	I	A	N	U	N
E	C	O	U	P	A	S	A	Y	E	N	O
K	O	W	T	E	N	T	I	D	A	F	A
N	O	N	A	L	C	O	H	O	L	I	C
O	D	D	B	L	O	P	A	I	N	T	S

2	illegible	8	non-stop
3	impatient	9	misread
4	well-known	10	replay
5	low-fat	11	repay
6	non-alcoholic	12	unfit
7	misspell		

8 a)   C

b)

2   It sounds like a really difficult situation

3   Try not to worry too much

4   I know you must be really worried about

5   Is there anything at all I can do?

6   if that would help

module 3

Vocabulary

Verb and adverb combinations

1

2	up to	5	off	8	away
3	off	6	up to	9	off
4	along	7	around	10	home

Reading

A short break in Copenhagen

2 b)

1   No. 'with a vast number of pedestrianised streets, the best way to sightsee is by foot, or you may prefer a leisurely canal cruise … .'

2   Yes. You can tour the Carlsberg Brewery.

3   The Stroget and its side-streets.

4   Hotel Savoy. 'small, friendly hotel.'

5   Hotel Admiral. 'close to … the harbour.'

6   No. There are no tours to Kronborg castle on Saturdays in March.

7   £273.

8   It costs £18 and it takes 15 minutes

Grammar check-up

Past Simple, Past Continuous and Past Perfect in narratives

3

1   This happened one summer when three of us were travelling around Europe.

2   We were walking around a town when a man offered to change our money.

3   A friend had warned us never to change money on the street, but the man looked honest, so we decided to take a chance.

4   He pretended to give me fifty notes but I noticed that he had only given me forty-eight, so I asked him to count them again.

5   Ten minutes later we were sitting in a cafe when I realised that he had tricked us.

6   When he gave me back the money, he had replaced everything except the top two notes with newspaper!

The Present Participle

4

b   Who's that woman sitting over there?

c   Our next door neighbour saw the burglar climbing through an upstairs window.

d   Isn't that your son throwing stones at that car?

e   Pacific Airlines received hundreds of letters enquiring about the free flights offer.
f   From my bedroom I can hear lots of trains going by in the middle of the night.
g   I rushed into the kitchen because I could smell the toast burning.

Verb forms in narrative
Past Simple / Continuous, Past Perfect Simple / Continuous, Present Participle

5

2   tried
3   had been looking forward
4   had made
5   went
6   was having
7   cut
8   had been doing
9   hadn't won
10 made
11 couldn't
12 were planning
13 told
14 didn't speak

Continuous aspect in other tenses

6

c   I'll be staying
d   You've changed
e   tastes
h   I'll give
j   's painting

Pronunciation
Contractions and weak forms

7 a) 📼

1   *Daniel here. I'll be working late tonight so don't wait up for me.*
2   *This is Helen. Just to let you know, the flight's been delayed – it won't get in until 10.30.*
3   *It's Peter Crawford. I was just leaving the office when I got your message to phone, but I've obviously missed you.*
4   *This is Jenny McAdam. Thanks for your fax. Sorry, I'd forgotten all about the meeting, but I'll be able to make it.*
5   *Anna, it's Roger. I've been trying to get in touch with you all day. Where are you?*
6   *This is Simpson's Fabric Department. I'm afraid your curtains won't be ready for another week.*

Grammar snack
so / such

8 a)

| 2 | S | 4 | H | 6 | S |
| 3 | DT | 5 | DT | | |

b)

such a mess	such comfortable beds
so slowly	such a friendly tour guide
such loud music	so few places to eat
so much traffic	

c)

2	such terrible weather	5	so many times
3	such a good time	6	so much information
4	so crowded		

Improve your writing
Avoiding repetition

9 a)

TOKYO / 317

Tokyo

In the past few years, Tokyo has had more than <u>Tokyo's</u> fair share of problems – the financial <u>problems</u> in particular
5   have left <u>Tokyo</u> far less confident than <u>Tokyo</u> was in the mid-1980s.
    The good news, though, is that <u>Tokyo</u> is great value for money. Recently, visitors have
10 found that <u>Tokyo</u> has cheaper train fares and <u>has cheaper</u> shops than comparable cities in Europe <u>have</u>. The best way to start a tour is with an early visit to the fish and vegetable
15 market, which is called Tsukiji. <u>A visit to the market</u> is a good way to wake up, with all <u>the market's</u> noises and smells. Then satisfy your hunger with a plate of fish at one of the many lively <u>fish</u> restaurants around <u>the market</u>.
    If Japanese people want a peaceful escape from the
20 crowds, <u>Japanese people</u> go to nearby Hama Rikyu Teien, a <u>peaceful</u> traditional garden which is designed around small lakes. Then, if you want a complete contrast, try the glamorous shopping district, Ginza, but if you don't <u>want a complete contrast</u>, there are always more gardens at
25 Shinjuku Gyoen.

b) and c)

In the past few years, Tokyo has had more than its fair share of problems – the financial **difficulties** in particular have left **the capital** far less confident than it was in the mid-1980s.
    The good news, though, is that **the city** is great value for money. Recently, visitors have found that it has cheaper train fares and **less expensive** shops than comparable cities in Europe. The best way to start a tour is with an early visit to the fish and vegetable market, called Tsukiji. This is a good way to wake up, with all the noises and smells. Then satisfy your hunger with a plate of fish at one of the many lively **seafood** restaurants around.
    If Japanese people want a peaceful escape from the crowds, they go to nearby Hama Rikyu Teien, **a tranquil** traditional garden designed around small lakes. Then if you want a complete contrast, try the glamorous shopping district, Ginza, but if you don't, there are always more gardens at Shinjuku Gyoen.

module 4

Vocabulary
Qualities of mind

1 a)

noun	adjective
creativity popularity dependability	creative popular dependable
imagination determination	imaginative determined
loneliness impulsiveness inventiveness stubbornness awkwardness	lonely impulsive inventive stubborn awkward
art science	artistic scientific
intelligence confidence brilliance	intelligent confident brilliant
emotion logic	emotional logical

b)
2 determination
3 logical
4 stubborn
5 impulsiveness
6 confidence
7 awkward

Pronunciation
Stress patterns with suffixes

2 a) 📼

1 creativity		6 scientific	
2 popularity		7 artistic	
3 dependability		8 creative	
4 imagination		9 impulsive	
5 determination		10 inventive	

b)
2

Grammar check-up
Passives quiz

3
2 The Taj Mahal
3 The television
4 The Moon
5 Princess Diana
6 Poland

Passives

4

Text A
2 need
3 are specially formulated /
   have been specially formulated
4 contains
5 not be taken

Text B
1 has only recently opened
2 are offering
3 includes
4 is limited
5 be made

Text C
1 has been used
2 was believed
3 was used
4 believed
5 protect

Text D
1 was being investigated
2 complained
3 had eaten
4 had not been properly cleaned
5 are currently being treated
6 to be sent

Choosing active or passive

5

2	b	4	a	6	a
3	a	5	a	7	b

Improve your writing
Describing a traditional dish

6 a)

2	stir	4	sieve	6	beat
3	season	5	grate	7	drain

b)
In correct order: J, F, D, H, G, B, A, I, K, C, E

Listen and read
How to do magic tricks

7 a)
1 B   2 A   3 D   4 C

b)
Trick A = 6, 8   Trick C = 1, 7   Trick B = 2, 4   Trick D = 3, 5

c)
2 S
3 S
4 D (to mutter = to speak under your breath – you don't want people to hear;
   to announce = to speak loudly to a group – you want them to hear).
5 S
6 D (to set fire to = to make something burn – often something that is not supposed
   to burn, e.g. I set fire to the tablecloth; to catch fire = something begins to burn by
   accident, e.g. the tree caught fire in the storm).

Grammar snack
To have / get something done

8 a)
2 past   3 future   4 present

b)
2 We have / get our newspaper delivered every day.
3 I had two photocopies made of the article. / I had two photocopies of the article made.
4 Susan is having / getting some shelves put up at the moment.
5 I need to have / get this film developed as quickly as possible.
6 I'm having / getting some business cards printed tomorrow.

c)
2 Have you ever had your fortune told?
3 When did you last have your teeth checked?
4 Would you ever have part of your body changed?

module 5

Jazz chant
Verb noun word combinations

1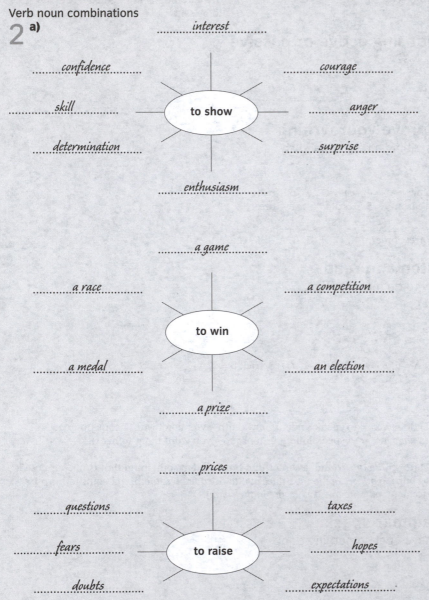

Verse 1: stress, job
Verse 2: flat, job, company
Verse 3: worthwhile, success, goals
Verse 4: banker, clerk, women
Verse 5: problems, shyness, fear

Dictionary work
Verb noun combinations

2 a)

interest

confidence   courage

skill   **to show**   anger

determination   surprise

enthusiasm

a game

a race   a competition

            to win

a medal   an election

a prize

prices

questions   taxes

fears   **to raise**   hopes

doubts   expectations

Future Perfect or Future Simple

3

a   she'll feel
b   I'll have lost, I'll have
c   will the photos be, won't have done
d   I'll have had, I'll give
e   I won't have had, I'll really need

Perfect tenses in the past, present and future

4 a)

2	d	6	a
3	f	7	e
4	g	8	b
5	h		

b)

3	have	a	hadn't
5	will you have	b	'd
7	Have	d	've
		g	won't have

Pronunciation
Contractions and weak forms

5 d)

1   *How long have you known her?*
2   *Have you been to the bank today?*
3   *How long has he been waiting?*
4   *Had she told you where she was going?*
5   *How long had they been married?*
6   *Have you tried hang gliding?*

Present Perfect Simple or Continuous

6

1   've only managed
2   've been making, 've lost
3   've failed, 've been studying
4   've been looking, 've only found
5   've been waking up, 've tried
6   's been behaving, 's started, 's stopped

Grammar snack
Just, still, by, so far and perfect tenses

7 a)

2   I'm sorry, but Mr Knowles has **just** gone home.
3   They were lucky because when they got to the station the train **still** hadn't left.
4   I've **just** read three chapters of the book you lent me. It's great! / **So far** I've read three chapters of the book you lent me. (so far) It's great!
5   **By** this time next year I hope I'll have found a girlfriend.
6   Even if we come back in an hour, she **still** won't have chosen a dress!
7   We had **just** arrived at the airport when the traffic controllers announced a strike.
8   Tom **still** hasn't sold his bike / **So far** Tom hasn't sold his bike (so far).

Reading
Books

8 a)

A A book club.

b)

2 Correct
3 Incorrect: 'The single thing we ask is that you buy at least one book from each Review magazine you receive during your membership.'
4 Correct
5 Incorrect: 'You'll have your books on ten days' approval before you need to pay for them. / Once you're satisfied, you pay for them …'
6 Incorrect: 'PLEASE SEND NO MONEY NOW'
7 Incorrect: 'Offer available in the UK only.'
8 Correct
9 Incorrect: *The Longman Dictionary of English Language and Culture.*
10 Correct

Improve your writing
Describing a book you have enjoyed

9 a)

1 adjectives to describe the story / book
2 types of book
3 adjectives to describe the writer

module 6

Vocabulary

1

2	e	5	a	8	i
3	h	6	g	9	j
4	f	7	d	10	c

2

1 (The) many people go to a gym regularly, to try to
2 lose (the) weight and cope with the stress of modern life.
3 Here are (the) some tips for finding the best gym for you.
4 Visit at least three clubs at the time of day you plan to work out. ✓
5 Check for (the) cleanliness, especially in the changing rooms.
6 Ensure the equipment is well maintained and suited to your ✓
7 requirements. Expect (the) well qualified, presentable instructors.
8 Check that an instructor is available in the gym area at all times ✓
9 for (an) assistance. Is the club security-conscious – do you need
10 an ID card to get in? Do you need to pay a membership fee and ✓
11 does the fee include the cost of aerobics classes? Choose a gym ✓
12 a short distance away – if it takes you more than (the) thirty minutes
13 to get there, you probably won't go. ✓

3

Text A	2	(–)	3	a
	4	a	5	The
	6	(–)	7	(–)
	8	a	9	(–)
	10	(–)	11	the
	12	the		
Text B	1	A	2	(–)
	3	(–)	4	(–)
	5	(–)	6	The
	7	(–)	8	an
	9	the	10	(–)

4

a At Christmas my mother usually goes to church at 8 o'clock, then she comes home and cooks a huge lunch.
b Deborah left home last year – now she works / is working as a lecturer in Vancouver.
c I visited Uncle Frank in hospital yesterday morning. He is very lucky, because he has got one of the best heart specialists in the UK.
d Is Jamie happy at school? Yes. He likes the teachers, and the school is five minutes away, in Kilmorie Road.
e Gordon is a terrible cook. He invited us for dinner last Saturday evening and it was one of the worst meals I have ever had.

Reading
Self-help books

5 a) c

b)

Picture A = Paragraph 4
Picture B = Paragraph 1
Picture C = Paragraph 5
Picture D = Paragraph 3
Picture E = Paragraph 2

c)

2	d	6	h
3	g	7	f
4	e	8	b
5	a		

Improve your writing
Taking notes: abbreviations

6 a)

2	a.s.a.p.	8	re.
3	&	9	a.m.
4	etc.	10	p.m.
5	Sat.	11	inc.
6	i.e.	12	P.S.
7	N.B.		

b)

2	a.m.	7	re.
3	etc.	8	i.e.
4	&	9	inc.
5	a.s.a.p.	10	P.S.
6	Sat.		

Writing notes

7

a 6.00 – Paul phoned. Wants to know if you're coming Anne's party Sat. – ring a.s.a.p.

b 10.30 Mr Larsen phoned. Plane arriving 9 not 8 a.m. Thurs.

c Gone to gym. Autoclinic phoned re. car – ready / Will be ready tomorrow p.m.

d 3 p.m. Susie phoned. Going to see *Godzilla* tonight with Paul. Meet you Shades wine bar 7 p.m.

Different ways of emphasising things

8 a) and b) 📼

Drew enters the flat, to see Jenny looking very upset. The noise of plates smashing, and screaming can be heard coming from the kitchen.

JENNY: Oh Drew, I'm **so** pleased to see you …

DREW: Why? What **on earth's** all that shouting in the kitchen?

JENNY: It's Simon – he's gone **completely** mad, because he thinks Anna's seeing someone else.

DREW: *(walking towards the kitchen)* Right, I'm going to stop this …

JENNY: *(running after him and pulling him back)* No, it's **far too** dangerous! He's got a knife!

DREW: You don't think he'll use it do you?

JENNY: I **really do** think he might, because he's been drinking … Anna's **absolutely** terrified.

DREW: *(walking around agitatedly)* This is ridiculous … let's try and talk to him.

JENNY: It won't do any good, he's **far too** drunk.

DREW: *(picking up the phone)* Okay then, let's call the police – there's **absolutely** nothing else we can do.

Emphatic constructions with *what* and *it* (cleft sentences)

9 a)

2 What I (really) feel like is a really nice hot bath.

3 It wasn't me who crashed the car.

4 What I've got here are our latest designs.

5 It was you who slept all through the play.

6 It was France who won the World Cup in 1998.

7 What impressed me about Sam was his enthusiasm.

b)

2 What I love about Autumn is the colour of the leaves.

3 It wasn't John who paid for the wedding ring, it was Sarah.

4 What you need is a new car.

5 Was it you who chose the furniture?

6 What I don't understand is how my sister paid for three holidays this year.

module 7

Vocabulary
Word building

1 a)

	Verb	Noun	Adjective
2	originate	origin	original
3	celebrate	celebration	celebratory
4	commemorate	commemoration	commemorative
5	participate	participation	participatory
6	fascinate	fascination	fascinating / fascinated
7	demonstrate	demonstration	demonstrative

	Noun	Adjective	Adverb
8	tradition	traditional	traditionally
9	history	historical	historically
10	—	international	internationally
11	commerce	commercial	commercially
12	atmosphere	atmospheric	atmospherically

b)

2 celebratory   6 commemorate

3 internationally   7 decorate

4 historical   8 atmospheric

5 commercial   9 demonstration

Pronunciation
Adverbs

2 a) 📼

1 The costumes are **historically** accurate.

2 The agreement is **internationally** recognised.

3 He died **tragically** in a car accident.

4 She argued her point of view very **logically**.

5 A speech is **traditionally** made after the wedding.

6 It's **practically** impossible to get tickets for the World Cup Final.

7 Peter reacted **emotionally** to the suggestion.

8 The benefits of vitamin B6 have been **scientifically** proven.

9 The new drug has been **clinically** tested.

Grammar check-up
Relative pronouns

3 a)

2 which / that   6 when

3 whose, who   7 which / that, which / that

4 which / that   8 whose

5 where

b)

2 A virus.   6 Thanksgiving Day.

3 A workaholic.   7 A tripod.

4 Popcorn.   8 A ladybird.

5 A police cell.

c)

You can leave out the relative pronouns in numbers 1, 4, 7 (the first *which / that* only) because they are the object of the verb.

Listen and read

4 a)

1 The man is wearing a hat, not holding it out for money.
2 The man looks happy, not miserable.
3 The man is not leaning on a stick.

b)

2 True: 'asked him to visit, whenever he liked'.   (line 8)
3 False: 'life-size picture'.   (line 11)
4 False: 'took advantage of Trevor's absence … .   (line 29)
  Then Trevor arrived …'.   (line 38)
5 True: 'a little red in the face'.   (line 38)

Non-defining relative clauses

5

Hughie Erskine (1), **who was a handsome but poor young man**, was in love with Laura Merton (2), **whose father had demanded £10,000 to allow them to marry**. One day Hughie visited his friend Alan Trevor. Trevor (3), **who was an artist**, was just finishing a portrait of a beggar. 'Poor old man!' thought Hughie, 'he looks so miserable,' and gave the man a pound (4), **which was the last bit of money he had**. The beggar smiled, 'Thank you, Sir, thank you.' Hughie spent the rest of the day with Laura (5), **who was rather annoyed because he had given away his last pound**, and he had to walk home because he had no money to pay for transport. That night he went to his club (6), **where he met Trevor**. Trevor told him that the *beggar* was in reality Baron Hausberg (7), **whose financial skills had made him a millionaire**. Hughie felt deeply embarrassed. The following day he received an envelope from the Baron (8), **which had this message written on the outside: 'a wedding present from an old beggar to Hughie and Laura'**. Inside was a cheque for £10,000!

Participle relative clauses

6

b Packages left unattended will be taken away.
c Is that your phone ringing?
d Anyone parking here will have to pay a £20 fine.
e All the people injured in the accident have been released from hospital.
f The conference taking place next week could change the future of the company.
g I like Martinis shaken not stirred.
h Most of the people invited to the wedding came to it.

Relative clauses

All types

7

A   COMEDY
The Comedy Experience, featuring / which features the brilliant Steve Simons and newcomer Martin Jones, finishes on Friday. Tickets, priced £8 and £12, are available on the door.

B   CINEMA
Terminator 2, starring / which stars Arnold Schwarzenegger, is an excellent sequel to the original *Terminator*. This version, which includes / including new special effects, is a 'must' for all Arnie fans.

C   OUTDOOR CONCERTS
The first concert in Crystal Palace Park features three groups whose music instantly brings back the atmosphere of the 1970s. Hot Chocolate, who are the main attraction, will be performing hits like *You Sexy Thing*.

Improve your writing

Punctuation

8

Not Too Old

Ⓐ woman who became Ⓑritain's oldest test-tube mother, has attacked critics of her plan to have a second child. Ⓒhristine Ⓣaylor, who told doctors she was forty-eight instead of fifty-five, described as 'stupid' people who said she was too old to look after another baby. Ⓢhe said, 'I feel just as energetic as when I had my first baby twenty years ago.'

Ⓢhe claims that her life with son Ⓡalph, conceived through fertility treatment in 1997, is just the same as a young mother's. Ⓗowever, she is worried that Ⓡalph might be embarrassed by his parents' age. 'Ⓣhat's why I want to have another child immediately,' she explains, 'so he'll have someone in the same situation.'

Ⓜrs Taylor, who has advertised locally for an egg donor, says she has had a good response.

Quantifiers

9

Rollerblades
2 quite a few   4 slightly too much   6 enough
3 plenty   5 too much   7 very few

Choc 'n' Nut Ice cream
1 loads   4 too much   7 too much
2 any   5 some
3 plenty   6 not nearly enough

CD Players
1 various   3 a few   5 any
2 any   4 very few   6 too many

Grammar snack
Used to / would + verb

10 a)

1	All correct	7	All correct
3	All correct	8	Incorrect: I'd spend
4	All correct	9	All correct
5	Incorrect: We'd live	10	All correct
6	Incorrect: I'd believe		

b)

2 On New Year's Eve we'd always stay up until midnight.
3 We never used to go abroad for our holidays.
4 The day I used to enjoy most was Christmas day.

module 8

Dictionary work
Word combinations: politics

1 a)

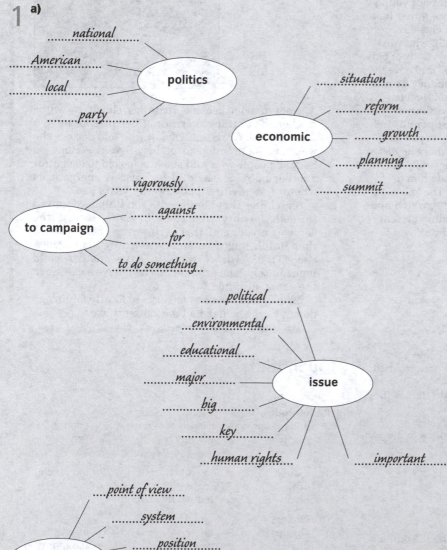

b)

2	economic	5	political
3	politics	6	issue
4	economic	7	campaign

Vocabulary
Word building

2

A Vote on May 9th!

2	government	7	qualified
3	unemployment	8	bureaucracy
4	inflation	9	corruption
5	economic	10	democratic
6	educational		

B Join Friends of the Earth

1	natural	6	environmental
2	supporters	7	campaigned
3	contributions	8	illegal
4	powerful	9	solutions
5	industrial	10	politicians

Pronunciation
Word stress and reading aloud

3 a) ▭

economy	economic
nature	natural
educate	education
contribute	contribution
qualify	qualification
industry	industrial
bureaucrat	bureaucracy
environment	environmental
democrat	democracy
politics	politician

Grammar check-up
Infinitive of purpose

4

2	c	5	f
3	b	6	d
4	e		

Infinitive forms

5

b I'd rather not talk about it, if you don't mind.
c You should've / should have brought your photos to show me.
d You'd better get some sleep – you've got a long day tomorrow.
e Maria's English seems to be improving.
f The film made Sonia feel very depressed.
g Picasso is thought to have painted this picture.

Patterns using infinitives with *to*

6

2	a chance	5	what	8	pretended
3	manage	6	tend	9	something
4	late	7	an effort	10	afraid

Infinitive or gerund (*-ing* form)

7

2	to create	5	be sent	8	make / to make
3	to provide / provide	6	to play	9	introducing
4	to get	7	helping	10	to stop

Reading

8 b)

1	to give	6	to do
2	to be chased, to leave	7	be included
3	to show	8	get
4	to tip	9	be
5	be asked, to carry, to make	10	suggesting, be included

c)

b	10	e	1	h	9
c	4	f	8	i	6
d	2	g	3		

Grammar snack

Plural nouns and collective nouns

9

2	h	haven't / hasn't	6	e	are / aren't
3	g	don't / doesn't	7	a	are / is
4	f	are	8	c	have
5	b	are / is, aren't / isn't			

Improve your writing

10 a)

(1) Many people have mixed feelings about having a national lottery in their country. (2) Thirty years ago in the United Kingdom the Government were against the idea, whereas nowadays people win millions of pounds every week.

(3) One of the strongest arguments for having a national lottery is that large sums of money can be given to good causes, such as sports facilities for the handicapped. (4) What's more, these are often the kind of charitable projects which otherwise would not receive much funding from the Government. (5) Furthermore, money can be used for the arts, for example by building new museums or redecorating theatres. (6) Another key point is the huge amount of enjoyment that thousands of 'hopefuls' get from participating.

(7) On the other hand, many people are concerned about the possible negative effects of the lottery. (8) They point to the great number of families on low incomes who can spend an excessive amount of their money on buying tickets. (9) In addition to this, it encourages people to pin all their hopes on their dream of 'a big win', instead of dealing with the day-to-day problems of real life. (10) One other important consideration is the enormous profits that the lottery companies make, in relation to the money they give away.

(11) In conclusion, I think it is difficult to see a clear-cut answer to this question. It probably depends on how serious a part of your life the lottery is.

b)

2	On the other hand,
3	Furthermore,
4	Another key point is
5	However,
6	One of the strongest arguments for

module 9

Vocabulary

Describing things that are odd or unusual

1 a)

2	upside down	8	torn
3	got stuck	9	a crack
4	the wrong size	10	a mark
5	broken down	11	melted
6	scratched	12	a hole
7	inside out		

b)

2	torn	8	melted
3	scratched	9	got stuck
4	inside out	10	a crack
5	upside down	11	a hole
6	the wrong size	12	a mark
7	broken down		

c)

2	mark / stain	5	crack
3	torn	6	stuck
4	stain / mark	7	way

Modal verbs

Revision

3

b	mustn't / shouldn't
c	might / could
d	shouldn't / oughtn't to
e	can't
f	can't
g	might / could
h	must / have to

4

b	might / could
c	should / ought to
d	can't
e	don't have to
f	should / ought to
g	must

Past modals

5

b must have been
c must have gone
d should have thrown / ought to have thrown / could have thrown
e must have had
f should have told / ought to have told / could have told
g might have eaten/ could have eaten
h might have been / could have been
i can't have read / couldn't have read
j shouldn't have eaten / oughtn't to have eaten

Past modals in everyday conversations

6

Conversation a
S: Where did you last have it?
P: I don't know. I used it last night when I bought a / my train ticket, so I must have had it then.
S: Have you used it since then?
P: No. I suppose I might have lost it on the train or I might have left it at home this morning.
S: Why don't you phone home and / to check?

Conversation b
S: Where have you been? It's 11 o'clock!
Z: I got stuck in (the / some) traffic.
S: Well, you should have phoned!
Z: I'm sorry, I left my mobile phone at home.
S: But if I'd known you'd be late (were going to be late), I could have gone to the pub.
Z: I'm really sorry.

Listen and read
Coincidences

7 a)

A 2   B 5   C 4

b)

2	C	5	C	8	C	11	B
3	B	6	A	9	A	12	B
4	A	7	A	10	C		

c)

2 through (line 7)
3 gone (line 9)
4 around (line 22)
5 dialled (line 26)
6 happened (line 28)
7 up (line 30)
8 stuff (line 32)
9 stuck (line 34)

Grammar snack
Need

8 a)

2 same   3 same   4 different

b)

2 need glasses / need to get glasses / need to wear glasses
3 needs a cut / needs cutting / needs to be cut
4 need to improve
5 needn't take / don't need to take
6 needn't have studied
7 don't need ironing / don't need to be ironed
8 needn't have brought
9 didn't need to wait
10 needs fixing / needs to be fixed

Improve your writing
Formal and informal letters rearranging plans

9 a)

> Magyar Porcelain Company,
> 1210 Budapest
> Brasso ut. 122 I/7
>
> 17th March 19..
>
> Ms. Hawley,
> Secretary to the Board,
> Magyar Porcelain Company,
> 3 Wessex Street,
> London SW1 1MV
>
> Dear Ms. Hawley,
>
> I am writing with regard to my forthcoming visit in May. As you know, I had originally planned to arrive on Thursday 14th and stay until Monday 18th. However, due to unforeseen circumstances, I am afraid that I will have to alter these arrangements. I will now be arriving on Friday 15th, staying until Tuesday 19th.
>   I would be grateful, therefore, if you would arrange for a car to collect me from Heathrow airport. My plane is due to land at 10.30 a.m. It will also be necessary to postpone the scheduled meeting on Friday morning to late Friday afternoon and to inform all the people concerned. If that is not possible, perhaps it could be arranged for Monday morning.
>   Finally, would you mind contacting my hotel to change the room booking.
>   I look forward to meeting you next month.
>
> Yours sincerely,
>
>
> Zoltan Biro
> Managing Director

> Paris,
> *Monday afternoon*
>
> Dear Mark,
>
> Hope you're well and looking forward to our weekend together. This is just to let you know something's come up at the office and I won't be able to get away until late on Friday. I've managed to get a ticket for a night train which gets into Waterloo early on Saturday morning. Don't bother to come and pick me up, I'll jump on a tube and make my own way to your place. If you have to go out just leave the key in the usual place.
>   This obviously means that we'll have to put off going to see Claire and Annabelle until Saturday – I hope you can sort that out. Oh, one last thing – will it be okay to stay until Tuesday morning? I'll assume it is, unless I hear from you.
>
> All the best,
> Chantal

module 10

Vocabulary
Organising an international event

1 a)

2	h	5	d	8	i
3	b	6	a	9	g
4	e	7	c		

b)

2	raise / profile	6	attracted / attention
3	publicise / event	7	compensate / for
4	appeal to people	8	sponsored by
5	lucrative / contract	9	high fee

Basic future forms
Will and *going to*

2

b	I'll lend	f	I'm going to work
c	I'm going to have	g	I'll think
d	I'll send	h	We're not going to sell
e	we're going to paint		

Going to and Present Continuous for intentions and arrangements

3

c	I'm really enjoying
g	I'm meeting
h	he's making

Phrases to express future ideas

4

b The Queen hopes to visit several hospitals during her trip.
c The Minister intends to spend more time with his family.
d Management negotiators don't expect to reach an agreement before Friday.
e The President has arranged to meet union representatives tomorrow.
f The Government is due to announce huge increases in petrol prices in the budget.
g The Government aims to cut unemployment by ten per cent this year.
h Florida is preparing to receive thousands of people made homeless by yesterday's earthquake.

Grammar snack
In case and *if*

5 a)

2	e	forget	5	b	overslept
3	d	got	6	c	happens
4	a	get			

b)

2	if	6	if
3	if	7	in case
4	in case	8	If
5	in case		

Future Simple, Future Perfect or Future Continuous

6 a)

2	will already have started	5	'll still be having
3	won't have finished	6	will know
4	'll have driven	7	'll be going

b)

1 Secretary: He's quite tall and **he'll be holding** a sign …
2 Tania: I'm sure **it'll be** okay.
3 Rikki: **I'll give** it to her then.
4 Jackie: **Will you have finished** …
Eleanor: Yes, by next Friday it'll be over, thank goodness, and **I'll be** my normal self again.

Pronunciation
Reading aloud: linking

7 b)

1 Secretary: When your plane gets in next Monday, a representative from our company, Mr Hashimoto, will be waiting for you.
Ms Jenkins: How will I recognise him?
Secretary: He's quite tall and he'll be holding a sign with your name on it. If you have any problems, just phone us immediately.

2 Mrs Gunner: I'm almost sick with worry.
Tania: What time's Henry's operation?
Mrs Gunner: At 3.00 this afternoon.
Tania: I'll be thinking of you both then. I'm sure it'll be okay.
Mrs Gunner: I hope so.

Reading
Fit for Life sports centre

8 a)

Membership for me, Susie and Rachel
£ 130

Swimming course for Susie
£ 24

Session in the Spa for me
£ 13.75

10 workout classes for Simon
£ 41

Induction and one visit to gym for me
£ 20.50

Squash court for Simon (half an hour)
£ 5.30

Total   £234.55

b)

2 7.30 p.m.
3 Yes, but it's ladies only.
4 No, she's too young.

5 Aqua, Tai Chi, Yoga.

6 No, training shoes only.

7 Circuits: 'recommended for sports specific training'.

8 No: 'Customers will not be allowed to enter the studio after the commencement of the class'.

9 No: 'Customers must be aged 16 and over to take part in our regular classes.'

10 No: the Circuits classes are from 7–8 p.m. on Wednesday and Thursday.

Improve your writing
Inviting a speaker

9 a)

Dear Mr Gough

I'm writing
I ~~write~~ on behalf of my school club ~~for~~ ask if you would be able to come and give 2

    a   s

us talk about your work with the team. Many of our member are keen fans and 2

         to

would love hear about the training and opportunities for amateur footballers. We 1

             every

have Social Club events ~~all~~ Wednesday evenings and we are looking for speakers 2

for 10th, 17th or 24th March.

                             s

If you are able to come, I suggest the talk ~~to~~ start at 7.30 (later if you wish, of 1

                       to

course) and lasts about an hour, including time for people ask questions. Also, 1

  would be   wards

we are delighted if you would join us for dinner after. 2

                                     would be

Please let us ~~to~~ know which date would suit you, and what ~~would be~~ your fee. 2

                                   ing

I do hope you will be able to come. I look forward to hear from you. 1

Yours sincerely,

....

Vocabulary
Sports and physical activities

10 a)

2 cycling   3 running   4 aerobics

b) 🔊

adjective	noun	verb
strong	strength	strengthen
confident	confidence	—
flexible	flexibility	—
competitive	competition / competitor	compete
trained	training	train

c)

2 e   5 f

3 d   6 b

4 a

module 11

Vocabulary
Medicine and science

1 a)

verb	noun
test	test
replace	replacement
cure	cure
eliminate	elimination
treat	treatment
spread	spread
prevent	prevention

b)

2 We'll have to test the rest of the family for hepatitis.

3 Johann never lets his disability prevent him **from** enjoying life.

4 Correct.

5 Correct.

6 Scientists are still no nearer finding a cure **for** AIDS.

7 Correct.

8 One of the government's aims is the prevention **of** alcohol consumption by under fourteen-year-olds.

c)

1 with

2 prevent / from

3 tested for

4 spread through

5 cure for

6 cured of

Talking about hypothetical situations (using *if*, *supposing* and *imagine*)

2 a)

2 a could

3 c might, might

4 g were

5 h could

6 d were, would

7 b couldn't

8 e could

Talking about hypothetical situations (using *I wish* and *if only*)

3

b If only I could drive.
c I wish Sally would speak up. I can hardly hear her.
d I wish I were / was at home now.
e If only I didn't get so nervous before exams.
f I wish you would shut up and listen to me.

It's time

4

b It's time we went home.
c It's time the children were in bed.
d It's time Jo realised that money doesn't grow on trees!
e It's time you learnt to cook for yourself!
f It's time I got / bought / had a new watch.

Talking about hypothetical situations in the past (using *if*)

5

1 b they would still be together now.
2 a we wouldn't be in such a mess.
   b the stock market wouldn't have collapsed.
3 a I'm sure he'd be fitter.
   b he'd have saved / he would have saved a fortune.
4 a I could give you a lift to the station.
   b she wouldn't have been able to go to Cambridge.
5 a she wouldn't have lost them all.
   b she wouldn't be retyping them now.

Talking about hypothetical situations in the past (using *I wish* and *if only*)

6

2 I wish I'd brought my / an umbrella.
3 I wish I hadn't come (here).
4 If only I hadn't eaten all the / those chocolates.
5 I wish I hadn't bought this dress.
6 If only I'd studied harder.

Talking about hypothetical situations in the present and past (using *I wish* and *if only*)

7

b hadn't   d had   f was / were
c would   e could   g wasn't / weren't

Reading
The science of chronobiology

8 a)

2 True   4 False   6 True
3 False   5 True   7 True

b)

The following activities are in the wrong time period:
6 a.m. – 8 a.m.   have a shower, do a workout
8 a.m. – 1 p.m.   try a new restaurant, drink alcohol
1 p.m. – 5 p.m.   play tennis
5 p.m. – 8 p.m.   —
8 p.m. – midnight   study, eat
midnight – 6 a.m.   to sleep, clean your teeth, do a workout

Improve your writing
Reporting opinions

9 a)   Article B

b)

2 Do you really learn English by studying on your own? Why?
3 Paragraph 1 To introduce the topic.
   Paragraph 2 To give the results and the case for the coffee bar.
   Paragraph 3 To give the case for the quiet study room.
   Paragraph 4 To draw a conclusion.
4 8 times
   Possible answers: students, two, the overwhelming majority, some, others, most, they
5 apart from: to show an exception
   some … others: to make a contrast
   especially if: to give emphasis
   Whilst a few … most: to make a contrast
   All in all: to summarise
   although: to make a contrast

module 12

Vocabulary
Prefixes and suffixes

1 a)

un-	in-	ir-	-less
unpredictable	inaccurate	irresponsible	harmless
unreliable	insensitive	irrelevant	thoughtless
unsuitable	inoffensive		
uninformative	intolerant		
unconvincing			
unaware			
unappealing			

b)

2 predictable
3 unsuitable
4 irrelevant
5 insensitive / thoughtless
6 harmless
7 biased

Pronunciation
Word stress

2 a)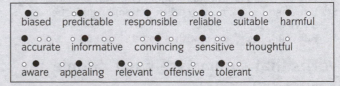

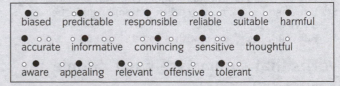

Listen and read
Attitudes towards television

3 a)

2 Emily
3 Guy
4 Emily
5 Veronica
6 Guy

b)

2 a couch potato   (line 33)
3 odd   (line 37)
4 revolves around   (line 2)
5 a series   (line 12)
6 a fly-on-the-wall documentary   (line 13)
7 withdrawal symptoms   (line 20)
8 a consumer watchdog programme   (line 58)
9 a cockroach   (line 58)
10 vying for   (line 61)

c)

1 No: 'we banned it completely'   (line 30)
2 They waste less time and they have more to do in their lives   (lines 41–45)
3 She watches them all day on Sunday to catch up   (lines 17–18)
4 Yes: 'I do have a social life of sorts'   (line 19)
5 Somebody put it there deliberately   (lines 58–59)
6 To get a bigger audience and make more money   (line 61)

Vocabulary
The media

4

2 cartoonist
3 headlines
4 a novel
5 take the TV off
6 live

Reporting people's exact words

5 a)

A **rude or cheeky:**
   4 Jimmy asked me if I'd give him a kiss.
B **flattering or complimentary:**
   5 Michael said he thought I had beautiful eyes.
   6 Andi added that I was the best teacher he'd ever had.
C **ridiculous or unfair:**
   2 My boss told me he was going to reduce my salary.
   3 She said I'd cheated in the exam.

b)

2 I thought you said you'd been / there to New Orleans.
3 But you said you didn't want one / an ice-cream.
4 But I was told it / the room would cost £40.
5 But when I spoke to you earlier, you said he'd be free at 3 o'clock.
6 But you told me just now that you'd posted it.

Verbs that summarise what people say

6 a)

2 denied
4 blamed
5 persuaded
7 assured
10 agreed / decided

b)

2 She refused to pay.
3 She denied breaking the photocopier.
4 She complained that the food was undercooked.
5 She warned Pat that the roads were very slippery. / She warned Pat to be careful because the roads were very slippery.
6 She threatened to call the police (if they didn't turn that noise down).
7 He offered to have a look at my TV.
8 She blamed Geoff for the misunderstanding.

Grammar snack
Passive reporting verbs

7

b The terrorists are believed to be hiding somewhere south of the city.
c The rebel troops are thought to be only a few kilometres from the city.
d It is understood that the two Prime Ministers are close to reaching an agreement.
e The air traffic controllers' strike is expected to end in the next few hours.
f *Citizen Kane* is considered by many to be the best film ever made.
g It is claimed that this new drug increases your life expectancy.
h Mick Riek and Mel Court are said to be honeymooning in the Bahamas.
i Thousands of people were reported to be homeless after the flood.

Improve your writing
Correcting written information

8 a)

2 To begin with
3 therefore
4 Secondly
5 In addition
6 On top of all this
7 As for
8 whereas
9 All in all